Storms
and Man

Lothrop, Lee, & Shepard Co. / New York

FRANK ROSS, Jr.

Storms
and Man

ALSO BY FRANK ROSS, JR.

Space Science and You
Transportation of Tomorrow
Model Satellites and Spacecraft:
  Their Stories and How to Make Them
The World of Engineering
The World of Medicine
The World of Power and Energy
Young People's Book of Jet Propulsion
Superpower: *The Story of Atomic Energy*
Modern Miracles of the Laboratory

The author wishes to thank the following corporations, government agencies, museums, and universities for permission to reproduce the photographs in this book:

American Red Cross—pp. 36, 44, 67, 79, 80, 87, 90, 91, 98, 110
American Telephone & Telegraph Company—pp. 13, 33, 147, 148
Florida Cooperative Extension Service, University of Florida—p. 157
General Electric Company—pp. 158, 164, 165, 168
Museum of the City of New York—p. 145
National Aeronautics and Space Administration—pp. 58, 59, 60, 118, 171
National Center for Atmospheric Research—pp. 25, 116, 119, 133, 137, 156, 174, 175, 176
National Oceanic and Atmospheric Administration—pp. 2-3, 14, 17, 20 (top and bottom), 28, 38, 40, 41, 43, 48, 49, 52, 55, 56, 65, 70, 82, 89, 92, 93, 94, 96, 97, 100, 103, 104, 105, 107, 108, 111, 120, 122, 134, 135, 136, 154, 160, 161, 162, 163
New Mexico Institute of Mining and Technology—p. 167
The Port of New York Authority—pp. 138, 142, 151
U. S. Department of Commerce—p. 51
U. S. National Forest Service—pp. 130, 131
U. S. Navy—pp. 29, 34, 46, 61, 62, 63, 84, 85
Westinghouse Electric Corporation (Courtesy Burndy Library)—p. 129

Title page photograph:
When tornadoes pass over water areas they are called waterspouts. Two are shown arching out of storm clouds and exploding in the sea.

Contents

CHAPTER ONE

Storms, Winds, and Clouds

Storms represent nature in her angry moods. These moods—weather disturbances, to be more exact—vary in kind and intensity. Hurricanes, tornadoes, thunderstorms, and the storms of winter are among the more important. As a general rule, the atmosphere that blankets our earth is a stable mass even though it is composed of delicately balanced elements. When these elements become unbalanced, for reasons largely unknown to the meteorologist, and a weather disturbance is caused, death and destruction often result.

Because man's existence on this planet is so directly affected by weather, he has always been interested in the forces that make it. Long before weather forecasting became the exacting, broad scientific field that it is today, weather prediction was an individual activity. It was practiced especially among those to whom weather was vital for their work—farmers and fishermen, for example. They did surprisingly well in predicting daily weather conditions simply by observing the nature of the clouds and the direction and force of the wind.

Many people, particularly the elderly, still supplement official weather forecasts with observations of their own, using their bodies as a kind of barometer. With them, an aching knee or shoulder is a painful signal that the weather is about to change.

But there is a good deal more to be learned about the weather than simply what it might be like tomorrow. Those who studied weather with a scientific attitude quickly found this out. The need

11

for knowledge was brought home with extra force whenever nature lashed out with a severe storm. During the course of one of these intensely dramatic events, winds of tremendous force and deluging rains often undid the work of man in a matter of moments. More importantly, storms showed that they could easily kill as well as destroy.

It was primarily because of the shocking number of human deaths resulting from major storms and the enormous property destruction that many weather scientists concentrated their studies on these atmospheric disturbances.

From the earliest years a number of scientifically minded men have contributed significantly to knowledge concerning the origin, structure, and movement of storms. We have space here to tell about only a few of the more outstanding of these gentlemen. One participant in that select group was the versatile Colonial American, Benjamin Franklin. There were not many aspects of life that escaped the keen, curious mind of that notable man. Weather and its puzzling behavior was one of his special interests.

Franklin's experiment with a kite during a thunderstorm to determine whether lightning and electricity were one and the same is well known. Less familiar to most of us is his observation, believed to be the first in meteorology, that storms move from place to place and that their advance is not influenced by the winds prevailing in a local region.

It was in 1743 that Franklin came to this conclusion. On October 21 of that year an eclipse of the moon was scheduled for 9:00 P.M. over Philadelphia. When the time arrived for the eclipse, it could not be seen. An intense wind and rainstorm had struck Philadelphia earlier in the day and continued on through the night.

Franklin, of course, was disappointed. But his scientific curiosity was partly satisfied by the nature of the storm itself. Noticing that

A view of a New York City street after the great blizzard of March 12, 1888.

13

The majestic soaring clouds of an advancing thunderstorm.

the winds lashing Philadelphia blew from the northeast, he concluded that places northeast of Philadelphia must have been struck by the storm a good deal sooner. The eclipse therefore could not have been observed in cities or towns northeast of Philadelphia.

Benjamin Franklin wrote to his brother in Boston about the storm and how it had interfered with his desire to see the eclipse of the moon. When his brother wrote in answer, Franklin was surprised to learn that he had been able to observe the eclipse. Indeed, the storm had not struck Boston until quite some time after that astronomical event.

This news from his brother greatly aroused Franklin's interest in the storm. He began investigating its path of travel by corresponding with friends living in other cities along the Atlantic coast and by reading newspaper accounts of the storm. Franklin's research revealed that the "northeaster" had actually been a hurricane. More importantly, despite its northeast winds the storm had struck regions *southwest* of Philadelphia before arriving at that city. Places northeast of Philadelphia were not hit until the storm moved on.

From this knowledge Franklin decided that the northeast storms that struck New England and the states in the middle Atlantic coastal region from time to time did not actually come from the northeast but from the south and west. He further concluded that storm systems move along a regular path from place to place independently of local weather conditions.

Franklin's theory about northeast storms and the movement of storms in general eventually became a well-established fact in meteorological science. Today this knowledge enables us to forewarn those areas that may be in the line of advance of these destructive weather forces.

Another early student of storms was the American scientist James Pollard Espy. Conducting his investigations in the early decades of the nineteenth century, Espy is credited with being the first to recognize that convection—the rising of warm air masses to high altitudes—takes place in storms.

One of the more significant facts which early investigators of storms uncovered was their characteristic whirling pattern. That is, the basic cloud formations making up these weather disturbances move in a circular manner. A German physicist and meteorologist, Heinrich Wilhelm Dove, made the discovery that this circular motion of clouds followed a clockwise path in the Southern Hemisphere and a counterclockwise direction in the Northern Hemisphere.

In the late 1830's Captain Henry Piddington, while working for British shipping interests in India, studied the tropical storms of that region and noted the peculiar whirling manner of the storm clouds. He called such weather disturbances "cyclones," from the Greek word *kyklon,* meaning "whirling round," of which the cloud

15

formation reminded him. The word "cyclone" ever since has become a kind of basic word for all rotary storms such as hurricanes.

Just how apt a word Captain Piddington had selected for these tropical storms was not fully appreciated by weather experts until the advent of radar for meteorological studies. The radarscope made vividly clear the snakelike coil or circular pattern of hurricane clouds.

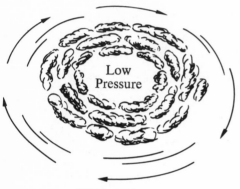

CYCLONE

Winds blow clockwise
in Southern Hemisphere

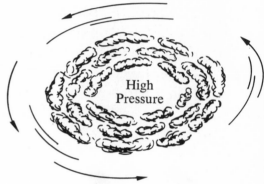

ANTICYCLONE

Winds blow counterclockwise
in Southern Hemisphere

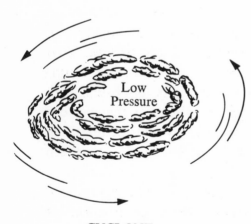

CYCLONE

Winds blow counterclockwise
in Northern Hemisphere

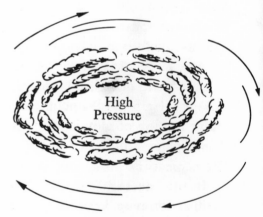

ANTICYCLONE

Winds blow clockwise
in Northern Hemisphere

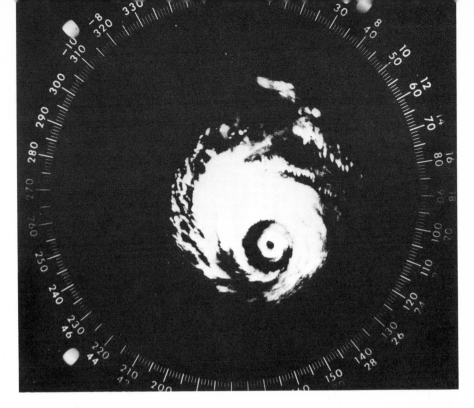

The National Weather Service's network of radar stations along the Gulf and Atlantic coasts is constantly alert for tropical storms during the hurricane season. This is a radarscope view of Hurricane Beulah as it approached the Texas city of Brownsville in 1967.

Early weather researchers specializing in studies on the origin and development of storms soon learned that a number of atmospheric conditions contributed to these disturbances. Of these there appeared to be three that were more importantly a part of storms than others—wind, falling barometric pressure, and clouds. They found these to be the main building blocks of storms; the way they were assembled determined the size and intensity of weather disturbances.

Wind is the horizontal movement of air over the earth's surface. Basically, the sun's energy output upon the earth has a great deal to do with wind movement. The earth's rotation also plays a role in this activity. Over particular localities, however, temperature variation and differences in barometric pressure are mainly responsible for the winds flowing more or less vigorously. In the case of two unlike air masses, a warm and a cool, with two equally unlike barometric readings of a "low" and a "high," the winds generated are quite often strong.

Since the invention of the barometer by Torricelli in 1643, barometric pressure readings have become vital data to meteorologists in their general forecasts of weather conditions and studies of storms. When we look at a weather map in our daily newspapers we see the words "high" and "low" in distinctive letters. The area marked off as "high" means that the air mass affecting that region is dense and heavy. It is comparatively cooler and drier than the air surrounding it. When this cooler air mass pushes into a region, it does so like a wedge under the warmer air. As a general rule, a "high" barometric pressure reading indicates a rising barometer and good weather.

The "low" that appears on the weather map tells us that the air of the region this encompasses is relatively warm and moist when compared to the air surrounding it or the air that it has displaced. Because it is warmer, the air is less dense than the cooler air. When the warmer air mass, or "low," becomes dominant over an area, it does so by simply flowing over the retreating cooler air. A low barometric pressure reading generally means a falling barometer and unsettled weather. Since the air of the "low" is warmer and wetter than the cooler air it displaces, it usually brings clouds and rain.

The region where two dissimilar air masses come in contact with each other and struggle for supremacy is called a "front." If the cool air mass triumphs, the front is known as a "cool front." It is a "warm front" when a warm air mass wins supremacy. The front is usually a very active weather region. Here may be found great turmoil, featuring such elements of disturbed weather as strong winds, dark, menacing clouds, rain, sleet, snow, thunder and lightning.

The winds of a storm, or those of a more gentle nature, which

18

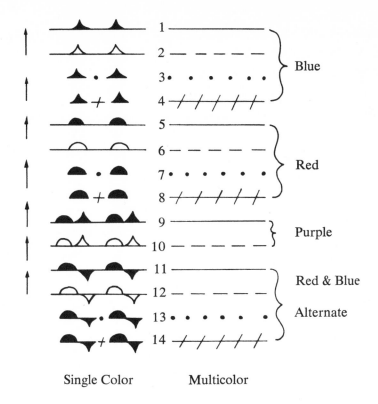

Single Color   Multicolor

SYMBOLS USED BY WORLD METEOROLOGICAL ORGANIZATION SHOWING KINDS OF FRONTS AND WEATHER ASSOCIATED WITH THESE FRONTS

KEY TO SYMBOLS

1. Cold front at the surface
2. Cold front above the surface
3. Cold front frontogenesis *
4. Cold front frontolysis **
5. Warm front at the surface
6. Warm front above the surface
7. Warm front frontogenesis
8. Warm front frontolysis
9. Occluded front at the surface
10. Occluded front above the surface
11. Quasi-stationary front at the surface
12. Quasi-stationary front above the surface
13. Quasi-stationary front frontogenesis
14. Quasi-stationary front frontolysis

* Beginning front   ** Dissipating front

Chart and Key adapted from *Guide*—World Meteorological Organization

When a cold front moves into a region of warm air, it is usually accompanied by strong, gusty winds. This unusual photo shows a cloud of wind-blown top-soil advancing with a cold front.

This pictogram graphically shows the major elements involved in the formation of a low pressure system or storm. Here a cold air mass is over-riding an area of warm air. Winds are beginning to form into a cyclonic pattern around a center of low barometric pressure.

we might experience on a warm summer's day, are more or less temporary and may come from just about any direction of the compass. However, there are other kinds of winds within our earthly atmosphere that are more permanent as to both velocity and direction. The trade winds over the Atlantic Ocean are a good example. In the Northern Hemisphere these blow toward the equator from the northeast, and in the Southern Hemisphere they blow in the direction of the equator from the southeast. The steadiest wind systems on earth, they are often referred to as the "northeast trades" and the "southeast trades." Captains aboard old-time sailing ships often made use of the trade winds for fast, dependable journeys to the New World.

In other areas of the world the winds may blow regularly for a long period from one direction, then, at another time of the year, change their direction to a completely opposite point of the compass. The monsoons (accompanied by heavy rains) in southeast Asia represent this type of wind system.

Different zones of atmospheric or barometric pressure are caused by the influence of the sun (responsible for the temperature variation), rotation of the earth, and locations of land masses and seas. The great prevailing wind systems in our atmosphere blow from the several zones of high pressure that are more or less permanent around the earth to zones of low pressure. Some of the major low and high zones over the Atlantic Ocean region include the doldrums, the horse latitudes and, above these, a low pressure belt extending nearly to the polar region.

The doldrums is a region of low pressure at the equator with little or no wind movement. As a matter of fact, the air movement there is likely to be vertical instead of horizontal. Intense solar radiation in this zone heats the air, causing it to expand and rise.

North of the doldrums is a zone of high pressure called the horse latitudes. This region is believed to have gotten its name in the days of the sailing ships when horses were a common part of the cargo. Traveling from Europe to America, vessels would often become

21

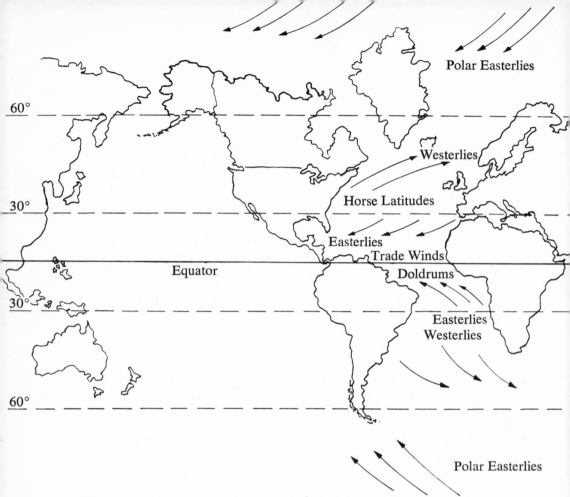

60°

30°

Equator

30°

60°

Polar Easterlies

Westerlies

Horse Latitudes

Easterlies

Trade Winds

Doldrums

Easterlies
Westerlies

Polar Easterlies

PRINCIPAL SURFACE WIND SYSTEMS OF THE WORLD

becalmed or move so slowly in the light, unpredictable winds of those latitudes that food and water supplies ran dangerously low. To conserve water, captains would order the horses killed and thrown overboard.

Above the horse latitudes lies another zone of low pressure. The polar front, with its cool air mass, is imbedded in this zone. Because of this, the region is one of considerable storm activity.

Although meteorologists tell us that winds flowing from high pressure areas to low pressure areas in particular regions do so in a more or less direct path, this is not the case with the great permanent wind systems of the earth. The winds travel from zones of high pressure to zones of low pressure at an angle rather than in a direct north or south line. The reason for this is the earth's rotation, which influences the path of the winds by what is known as the Coriolis force. The force is especially pronounced near the equator and causes winds flowing toward the tropical zone to be deflected to the right in the Northern Hemisphere and to the left in the Southern Hemisphere.

Direction and velocity are the two principal factors about wind that interest meteorologists, especially where storms are concerned. Direction of a blowing wind is obtained by the weather vane, with which most of us are familiar. This is simply a pointer that is turned by the flowing wind current and tells from which point of the compass it is coming. Many people with an amateur's interest in weather have the device attached to their rooftops or the top of a flagpole. It must be free from surrounding objects and high enough so that the wind striking the pointer will be a true wind force and not one that is deflected or bouncing from a nearby structure. The amateur's weather vane may also be quite ornamental, representing a whale, rooster, or horse and even such inanimate things as a boat.

The professional type of wind indicator may be no more than an arrow made of metal, fixed to and swiveling 360 degrees on a vertical shaft. Stationary letters, N, E, S, and W, representing the four major points of the compass, may be attached to the indicator. Whatever direction the arrow points to is the direction from which the wind is blowing.

Wind velocity is obtained by an anemometer, an instrument invented by an Irish astronomer and physicist in 1846. The device in use today by weather experts, although improved, is still basically the same as the original.

The anemometer consists of three or four hemisphere cups attached to arms extending out from a vertical shaft. This is rotated by the blowing wind. The revolving part of the instrument is connected to an electrical circuit that signals whenever the spinning

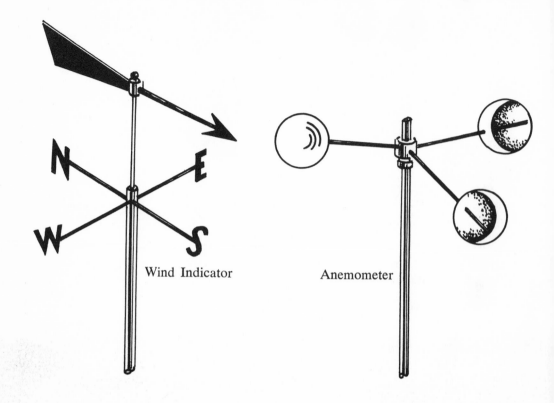

Wind Indicator

Anemometer

cups complete a revolution. The signals may be an electric bulb that lights up with every revolution, or a buzzing sound. Some also activate a pen that records revolutions on a drum.

By counting light-bulb flashes or buzzer sounds and using a special mathematical formula, the weather expert can figure out wind speed in miles per hour.

The anemometer is used by the weather forecaster to determine wind speed at the earth's surface. For higher altitudes, wind speed and direction are obtained with the help of a pilot balloon. The balloon is inflated with hydrogen or helium in such a manner that it will rise at a speed desired by the weather expert using it. With a theodolite, the balloon's vertical ascent is kept in constant view. The instrument is similar to the one used by land surveyors and permits the weatherman to read the balloon's elevation and azimuth (right or left angles) every minute. With the aid of trigonometry, the direction and speed the wind-driven balloon moves minute by minute can be calculated. The meteorologist calls the winds subject to this kind of study PIBALS, his special language for "pilot balloon observation."

Frequently the pilot balloon will be given an instrument and radio package to carry aloft. It is then called a radiosonde. This instrument records a variety of information such as wind speed and direction, temperature, and humidity, about the different levels of atmosphere through which it passes. The data is automatically

A launching of a helium-filled stratosphere balloon from the NCAR Scientific Balloon Flight Station at Palestine, Texas. These balloons are used to lift heavy equipment for scientific experiments to probe atmospheric and solar conditions in the stratosphere.

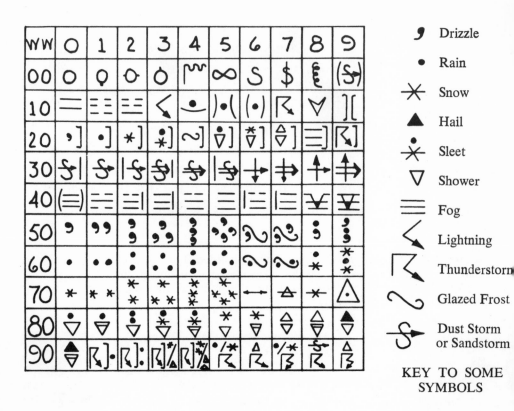

INTERNATIONAL WEATHER SYMBOLS

These weather symbols are used by meteorologists the world over. Weather conditions are transmitted by numbers at the side and top. Thus rain may be reported as 600, 601, or 602 and on up the scale, depending on its intensity and if mixed with sleet. Received at a central weather office, the numbers are decoded into the proper symbols which are then placed on a weather map. Chart adapted from *Guide*—World Meteorological Organization

transmitted to a ground station. The average height radiosondes may rise is sixty to eighty thousand feet. When the maximum altitude is reached, the balloon bursts and the instrument cargo floats to earth by means of a parachute.

Radar and radio direction-finding equipment may be used to track these high-soaring miniature weather stations. The meteorology tool is then referred to as a rawinsonde. The wind data gathered is called "rawins," short for radar or radio wind. The use of radar enables/weathermen to track rawinsondes right through dense cloud layers.

To non-professional weather observers, wind speed and wind force may be pretty much the same thing. Not so to the expert, however, since wind force, unlike velocity, tells him just how intense the flowing air current might be. This information is especially desired in the course of a storm. A variety of different methods were used by the early weather forecasters to determine this characteristic of winds. All were found wanting in one respect or another. Then in 1806 Sir Francis Beaufort, an admiral and hydrographer in the British Navy, originated a method that proved extremely successful.

Admiral Beaufort devised a numerical scale, from 0 to 12, which represented a gradual increase in the intensity of blowing winds. Each number also had a corresponding description of the nature of the wind. For example, zero was described as a calm. One indicated light air, and two was described as a gentle breeze. The scale continued on up to twelve—force twelve, as it was more accurately described—which indicated winds of hurricane force.

Beaufort's scale proved so successful that with slight modification it is used today by meteorologists and mariners the world over. The complete scale with its various representations may be found at the back of this book.

As one of the major elements in the formation of weather, particularly storms, wind cannot be seen but can be felt. This is not the case with that other chief factor in our changing weather patterns, clouds. Clouds are the visible bearers in the atmosphere of weather news. They tell when nature's mood is calm or disturbed. The beauty of clouds has inspired poets, and both children and grownups like to look at their infinite variety and imagine they see the shapes of castles floating through the sky or the images of people and animals. To the meteorologist, however, clouds are among the more important messengers telling what tomorrow's weather may be.

Clouds are formed when warm, moist air rises to high altitudes where its water vapor is cooled until it condenses into tiny droplets that are visible to the eye. When these droplets join others, clouds of varying sizes are formed. These droplets stay suspended in the atmosphere until air disturbances cause them to fall to earth. We shall have more to say on this in a later chapter. The shapes that clouds assume are, for the most part, the result of the horizontal movement of the wind. It is the wind that pulls and twists and flattens, working like the unseen hand of a sculptor.

Weather experts recognized the value of clouds quite early in the development of the science of meteorology. By studying certain characteristics of clouds, weathermen were able to gather information about wind direction and approximate velocity, and an indication of the temperature of the upper air levels and the moisture content. With the help of clouds, meteorologists could tell both the nature of the immediate weather and what it would be in several days. Some students of clouds even acquired the ability to predict storms simply by the shape and speed of movement of clouds. Cloud study became and is today an extremely important area of weather research and forecasting.

The swirling, churning clouds of a hurricane.

The feathery strands of cirrus clouds spread across the sky, high above a Hurricane Hunter plane.

At the beginning of weather science, cloud observation and study was not a simple activity. This was mainly because of the great variety of these masses of condensed vapor in the atmosphere. There was confusion as to what cloud shapes brought on what kind of weather conditions. Matters remained so until 1803 when Luke Howard, an English student of weather who was especially fascinated by cloud forms, brought order to the chaos by a system of classification. Howard placed clouds by shape or ap-

29

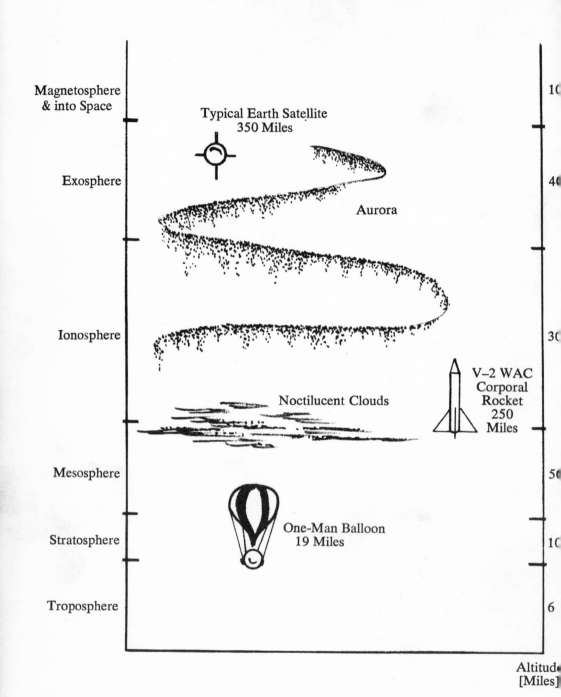

ATMOSPHERE LAYERS OF THE EARTH

pearance into three general types: cirrus ("lock of hair"), stratus ("layer"), and cumulus ("piled up"). Clouds are also referred to today as high clouds (cirrus), middle clouds (stratus), and low clouds(cumulus). There are numerous variations within these major groups, modifications made since Howard's time by other meteorologists.

Classification and current knowledge of cloud forms can be found in the International Cloud Atlas, produced by the World Meteorological Organization, Geneva, Switzerland. In this cloud forms are listed not only according to altitude but also according to their stability. Thus we find cirrus and cirrostratus as both high clouds and also the most stable. These exist at heights of 4 to 8 miles. Their moisture content is in the form of ice crystals.

In the middle group are such clouds as altostratus and altocumulus. They range in height from 2 to 4 miles. Their visible form contains moisture in several varieties—water droplets, rain, ice crystals, and snowflakes.

The lower clouds include stratus, nimbostratus, and stratocumulus. Cumulus clouds are a special class in this category. They can have a low base of a little more than a mile above the earth and extend upward to a height of three or four miles. At that altitude they become cumulonimbus, our well-known thunderstorm clouds. This type is formed rather quickly by massive vertical updrafts of warm, moist air.

The nacreous and noctilucent clouds are the highest of all. Meteorologists do not know how they are formed but since they exist far above the troposphere, the weather zone of our atmosphere, they do not play a part in the formation of weather. Their usual realm is from 14 to 60 miles high, closer to the world of outer space than the earth world.

When winds and clouds combine in particular ways, they help to produce a variety of weather disturbances. One of their major productions is the hurricane, a storm of great power and destructiveness.

CHAPTER TWO

The
Hurricane

The hurricane represents nature in one of her angriest moods. The severity of its major characteristics—size, fierceness of its winds and rain, and the length of time it may rage—makes the hurricane the mightiest of all weather disturbances that sweep over the face of the earth. Spawned over tropical seas and fueled by the heat and moisture of the equatorial region, the hurricane may grow to an immense size, spanning hundreds of square miles. Carried along by one of the earth's great wind systems as well as by its own energy, this tropical storm can travel for days and weeks to perform its devastation over land areas.

In the Northern Hemisphere the natives of the West Indies, Mexico, and the southeastern portions of what is now the United States were familiar with the awesome power of the hurricane long before the white man came to the New World. Many of these Indian civilizations were so impressed by the size and intensity of this storm that they made it a part of their religion. The Mayas of Mexico, for example, made the hurricane their storm god. Their word for this mythological figure was *Hunraken,* meaning "the big wind." Other Indian civilizations had similar terms to describe this great drama of nature—*Hyuracan, Hurakan,* and *Aracan.*

Columbus was one of the earliest Europeans to experience and tell about the tropical hurricane. He encountered several of these mammoth storms on his numerous voyages to and from the New World. Later, when the Spaniards came to the Caribbean area and heard one of the more common Indian words for this enormous

Lashed by the winds of a tropical hurricane, surging seas batter their way down a Miami street.

storm, *Huracan,* they adopted it into their language. Eventually, after passing through various transformations, this became our present-day word, hurricane.

"Hurricane" is the most common word in use in the Western Hemisphere for describing this tropical disturbance, but the storm is not restricted to this part of the world. It occurs in other regions where it is referred to by different names. In the far west Pacific, especially off the China coast and over the seas near Japan, the same kind of storm is called a typhoon. This is believed to have come from the Chinese word *tai-fung,* meaning "great wind." It was William Dampier, a widely traveled seaman, who first noted in 1687 the similarities of the hurricane and the typhoon. He had sailed through both storms and survived to tell about them.

From time to time the typhoon roars over the Philippines, where people call it the *baguio.* The Australians, who also experience the destructive power of this tropical disturbance, have given it the colorful name "willy-willy." Finally, a storm of similar character

33

sweeps out of the Indian Ocean where it is referred to as a cyclone, a memento of Captain Piddington.

The hurricane or tropical cyclone occurs not only in different parts of the world but also at particular times or seasons of the year. This is because of the close relationship between the sun, the major source of energy for starting these massive storms, and its yearly travels north and south of the equator. When the sun is at its farthest southward point in the Southern Hemisphere, the tropical cyclone season in the southern Pacific and Indian oceans is in full swing.

The far southwest Pacific is somewhat of an exception to this, however, since here the typhoon season is an all-year-round activity. The only variation concerns the intensity of the storms. Meteorologists in that part of the world have learned that the worst period is from June through October, when numbers of these vio-

The swirling center of Hurricane Gracie, September, 1959. Photo was taken from above the storm by a weather plane.

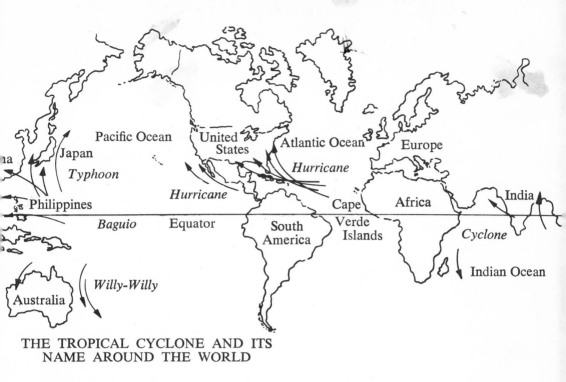

Pacific Ocean United States Atlantic Ocean Europe

Japan *Typhoon* *Hurricane*

Philippines *Hurricane* Cape Africa India

Baguio Equator South America Verde Islands *Cyclone*

Australia *Willy-Willy* Indian Ocean

**THE TROPICAL CYCLONE AND ITS
NAME AROUND THE WORLD**

lent disturbances may smash into the Philippines or blow their way
west and north to devastate Chinese and Japanese coastal areas.

In summer, when the sun is at its most northerly position in the
Northern Hemisphere, the hurricane season for this region com-
mences. Specifically, those areas of the United States along the Atlantic and Gulf coasts can expect to be hammered from time to
time by powerful tropical cyclones. The same expectation is shared
by those countries fronting on the Gulf of Mexico and within the
Caribbean Sea area. The hurricane season for this part of the world
generally runs from June through November.

At the beginning of the season, the Gulf of Mexico and the
Caribbean Sea are the main areas for the start of tropical cyclones.
As the season advances through July and August, the hurricane
spawning grounds shift farther eastward to the warm waters of the
southern Atlantic Ocean. With the coming of September and fall,
the peak of the season, hurricanes may originate anywhere in the
areas around the Bahamas, the Lesser Antilles, and to the eastward

35

The waters of Biscayne Bay, Florida, whipped to a fury by a hurricane that struck in September of 1948, pound over the sea wall.

as far as the Cape Verde Islands off the northwest coast of Africa.

Southwest of Mexico, where a much weaker type of tropical cyclone originates, there is another hurricane season in the spring and summer. As a rule, most of these disturbances die at sea or diminish in intensity as they travel over the desert areas of Lower California. Occasionally some will make their way as far north as the lower coast of the state of California, by which time they are no longer a true hurricane but simply a heavy wind-and-rain squall.

36

Sometimes these same storms will veer off course to lash the west coast of Mexico, causing a considerable number of deaths and property damage. Pushing northward into southwestern United States, the remnants of the hurricanes occasionally create damaging floods, especially in Arizona and New Mexico.

Meteorologists know a great deal about hurricanes. But one area of knowledge concerning these storms that mystifies them is how they start. Weather experts are familiar with the conditions necessary for the creation of these storms, such as low barometric pressure and rising currents of warm, moist air, but they do not know what factors are responsible for throwing these delicately balanced and complex conditions out of their normal equilibrium and into the beginnings of a powerful tropical cyclone.

After the disturbance begins, warm, moist air rises vertically within it in ever larger and faster quantities by the process called convection. As the air reaches higher and higher altitudes, water vapor condenses and the clouds of the young storm start to form. Almost from the very beginning of the disturbance, the clouds begin to assume the distinctive spiral pattern of the hurricane.

In the cloud-forming stage much heat energy is released, which increases the rate of speed of the clouds spiraling around the storm's center. As mentioned earlier, the clouds circulating within a hurricane in the Northern Hemisphere do so in a counterclockwise direction. In the Southern Hemisphere the clouds circulate in a clockwise path.

The hurricane is intensified or fueled by warm, moist air flowing into its center at the bottom. The air spirals upward through the storm and, after adding to its enormous power, eventually flows out through the top of the disturbance much as smoke comes out of a chimney. Meteorologists compare this activity to that of a pump —a vital, churning action that keeps the storm alive and flourishing. At about 40,000 feet the cyclonic moving air loses its force and is carried away by other high-altitude winds to form an anticyclone system.

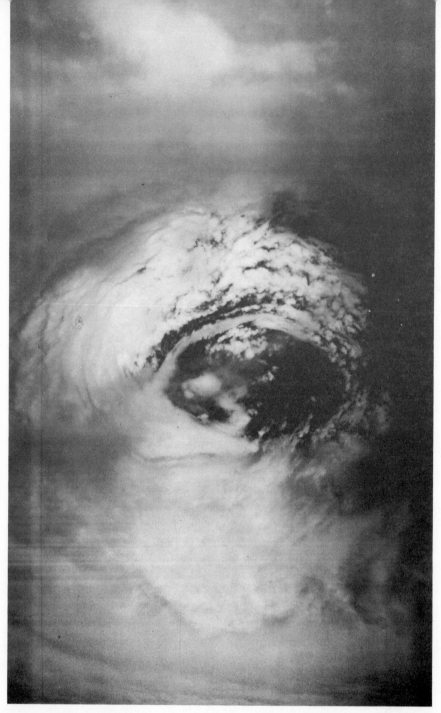

The eye and swirling rain clouds of Hurricane Betsy, a powerful tropical cyclone that roared out of the Atlantic in 1965. This photo of the center of the storm was taken by a USAF weather patrol plane from an altitude of over 11 miles.

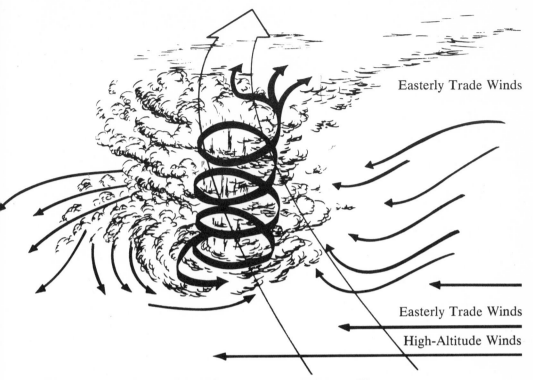

Easterly Trade Winds

Easterly Trade Winds

High-Altitude Winds

START AND DEVELOPMENT OF A HURRICANE
Adapted from *Hurricane*—ESSA, National Oceanic and Atmospheric
Administration

The present belief of hurricane specialists is that there exists a
definite relationship in the interaction of low-level and high-altitude wind systems that has much to do with the storm's growth in
power. If less air is pumped out through the top of the storm than
flows in at the bottom, the storm will choke itself and die. On the
other hand if more air is pumped out of the storm's theoretical
chimney, the disturbance will not only stay alive but grow to an
immense size and power.

A fully grown hurricane is an awesome spectacle. It has several
unique characteristics that set it apart from any other kind of
storm. Not the least of these is its spiraling cloud bands. These
swirl around a comparatively calm center, the well-known eye of

39

the storm, and are the bearers of immense cargoes of rain. The spiraling cloud bands form the heart of the hurricane and are driven by winds that gust from 74 miles per hour to more than 200 miles per hour. The region closest to the eye of the storm contains the most powerful winds. Their maximum force has never really been determined because no weather instruments have ever been able to withstand their power.

The spiraling cloud bands are separated by light areas within which little or no rain falls. The clouds are of the cumulus and cumulonimbus variety, the kind which build up into the towering formations of the thunderstorm. The hurricane clouds swirl upward around the eye of the storm in violently churning layers. They may rise to the topmost limits of the storm, 30,000 feet or more, where the cold of the higher altitude freezes the water vapor

The power of hurricane winds wrapped this piece of sheet metal around a utility pole like a piece of cloth.

Hurricane winds may gust to more than 200 m.p.h. With this wind velocity freakish things can happen. This photo shows a palm tree pierced by a 10-foot-long pine board.

into ice crystals. At their maximum height the clouds are transformed into the cirrus type.

The entire band of spiraling clouds of the hurricane may extend as far as 100 miles. Sometimes they go beyond this range. The winds, the most impressive part of a hurricane, blow with unimaginable ferocity within this area. Their velocity is given the number

12 on the Beaufort scale, indicating that they are blowing at a speed of not less than 74 miles per hour. This is the wind speed that gives a tropical storm its hurricane status.

However, this Beaufort reading tells only part of the story of the true nature of a hurricane. Very often the winds of such a tropical storm will blow at a rate of better than 200 miles per hour. When they do, few man-made structures or even nature's sturdiest handiwork can withstand the battering.

Beyond the edge of the hurricane's center there is another area dominated by winds of gale force—above 40 miles per hour. This portion of the hurricane may extend for 400 miles. The weakest of the storm winds are those on the outer perimeter of the cloud bands. These have been found to blow at a speed of hardly more than 30 miles per hour.

When the immense tropical cyclone moves over the earth's surface, its disruptive forces can affect land, sea, and air conditions over tens of thousands of square miles.

As we know, differences in atmospheric pressure are an important factor in the production of winds. Differences in atmospheric pressure are determined by barometric measurements and for this reason are also referred to as barometric pressures. The rate at which this pressure changes between points over a specific distance is called the pressure gradient. The winds flow along this gradient, usually from a high-pressure to a low-pressure point. In no other weather disturbance, excepting the tornado, does the pressure change take place so drastically as in the hurricane. At the birth of this tropical cyclone, it is the drop in atmospheric pressure at what eventually becomes the storm's core that causes winds to flow toward it. Convection whirls the winds upward and the storm is on its way.

Of all the characteristics of the hurricane the most unique is its calm eye. No other weather disturbance has this feature. While the furiously raging hurricane winds are spinning in their destructive tracks, the eye in their center remains a calm haven where little or no wind exists. Above the eye the sky may even be cloudless with patches of blue showing. The eye of an average hurricane may extend for almost 14 miles. In some storms, eyes almost double this diameter have been found.

Because it is free of any destructive forces, the eye gives the hurricane a rather tricky nature. When this portion of the tropical cyclone passes over a locality, people often feel that the storm has blown over. As many have learned to their regret, such is not the case. Just as soon as the eye goes by, all the storm's previous ferocity resumes. In fact, with the winds blowing from a different quarter, they may be even more powerful than before.

It is in the eye of the hurricane that the storm's lowest barometric pressure readings are found, along with the highest temperatures. Indeed, hurricanes are usually record breakers when it' comes to low barometric measurements. At the peak of a particularly vicious hurricane that swept over the Florida Keys in September of 1935 a low reading of 26.35 inches was recorded.

This is a cross-section view of a hurricane as seen on the viewing scope of radar. Notice the generally clear eye of the storm. Height of hurricane clouds is more than 35,000 feet.

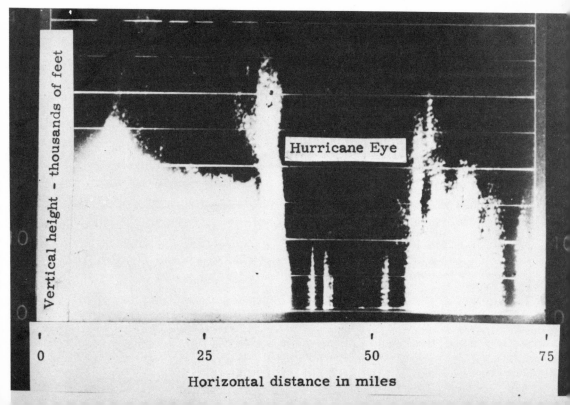

Vertical height – thousands of feet

Hurricane Eye

0   25   50   75

Horizontal distance in miles

Hurricane Donna battering Florida palm trees. With wind gusts of more than 180 m.p.h., this tropical storm of September 1960 left a path of death and destruction from Puerto Rico to New England.

The significance of extremely low barometric readings can be appreciated when it is understood that in the temperature zones the column of mercury in the barometer does not vary much above or below 29.00 inches. In the tropics the mercury reading is even more stable, remaining for days on end close to 30.00 inches. Only when a weather disturbance like a hurricane comes along does the barometer begin its drastic fluctuations.

When hurricanes sweep over land and sea, people are not the only living creatures who feel its destructive effects. Animals and birds, especially birds, suffer enormously from the storm's blows. It is not uncommon for hurricanes sweeping northward from the Caribbean to carry tropical birds hundreds of miles from their normal habitats. Many have been found as far north as New England after the passage of one of these tropical tempests.

Many unusual happenings occur during the course of a hurricane. Birds trapped in the spiraling winds can be helplessly blown into the storm's calm center. A ship passing through the eye of the disturbance will become a haven for the exhausted creatures. On a number of occasions seamen have reported seeing literally hundreds of birds drop down on the upper section of the ship, covering much of the superstructure.

As mentioned earlier, hurricanes spread over an immense expanse of the atmosphere. At the beginning stage of their formation their forward movement is aided by the flow of one of the great planetary wind systems. The northeast trade winds, for example, are closely involved with the hurricanes that start in the tropical waters of the North Atlantic and in the Caribbean Sea. In the initial development stage the forward speed of a hurricane is rather slow, usually no more than 15 miles per hour.

Hurricanes originating in the region of the West Indies will generally veer away from the equatorial zone and head in a northwesterly direction. As they approach the middle latitudes, their speed may increase to more than 60 miles per hour, though not many attain this extreme velocity.

Meteorologists who have devoted their careers to the study of these tremendous weather disturbances have paid special attention to a hurricane's speed of movement and the path it takes. It was hoped that a kind of pattern might be revealed by noting and analyzing the paths—or tracks as they are better known—taken by hurricanes over a period of many years. If this turned out to be the case, then a big step would have been taken in the task of trying to predict the direction in which these destructive storms are headed. Rather than contributing help in this area of hurricane study, however, the analyses showed that these tropical cyclones are terribly unpredictable.

At the start of its journey out of the tropics, a hurricane may move forward, as we said, at an average speed of about 15 miles per hour. Then, perversely, it may stop and hover for a short time over an area. Picking up speed again, the cyclone can resume in the same direction, or strike out along a new track, or even double back in the direction from which it came. To a weatherman, the unpredictability of a hurricane is horribly frustrating and even though he is aided by the most sophisticated of technical tools, he still finds it difficult to give adequate warning to inhabited areas that might lie in the path of the roaring wind-and-rain storm.

How long do hurricanes stay alive? Like their speed and direction of movement, this feature of tropical cyclones is rather difficult to determine. Through study of past hurricanes over a period

A U.S. Navy weather plane carefully observing and recording the movements of a hurricane.

DEATH OF A HURRICANE

When a hurricane moves inland it loses heat energy from the sea. Mountains and other land barriers also reduce the storm's power by friction. The spiraling clouds break apart, then move in different directions in small groups. With diminishing winds, the hurricane enters its final stage.

Adapted from *Hurricane*—ESSA, National Oceanic and Atmospheric Administration

of many years, weather scientists have been able to devise a reasonably dependable schedule of a hurricane's life expectancy. They have found that hurricanes spawned in the month of August stay in existence for about 12 days. Those born in July or November have a life span of about 8 days.

As long as a hurricane remains over warm tropical seas, it will stay alive and even intensify. Just as soon as it moves over land, the storm has entered upon its death stage. The reason is that the cooler land does not supply the storm with moist heat energy, the fuel necessary for the cyclone to flourish, which the tropical seas provide. This is the main cause of the storm's ending. Another, to a lesser degree, is the friction which the land mass in the path of the hurricane provides to help slow its movement. Hilly terrain, trees, buildings, all contribute to this friction, or braking effect.

Boats become frequent victims of tropical storms roaring in from the sea.

Does this mean that if a hurricane should avoid moving in over a land area and stay at sea instead, it would last indefinitely? No, for it will eventually die when it travels over cooler waters of the middle latitudes. Weather experts have discovered that these tropical storms will not form over water whose temperature is less than 80 degrees Fahrenheit. The cool air of the middle latitudes will flow into the center of the hurricane and put out its fire, so to speak. Hurricanes that reach higher and cooler latitudes, rather than die completely will be transformed into what weathermen call extratropical cyclones. These can be destructive but hardly on the scale of the tropical hurricane.

Newspaper photographs or television scenes can give excellent evidence of the power and destructiveness of hurricanes. But to appreciate the immense energy and fierceness of these tropical cyclones it is necessary actually to live through one. Scientists have estimated that the heat energy resulting from the condensation con-

48

stantly going on within the confines of the storm, in just one day in the life of the hurricane, is the equal of that released from the explosion of 400 20-megaton hydrogen bombs.

In more down-to-earth terms, if the energy produced and released within a hurricane in one day of its existence were to be converted into electricity, it would be sufficient to supply the electrical needs of the United States for more than six months. It is for good reason, then, that the hurricane has been called the greatest storm on earth.

Weary survivors of a hurricane being brought to a place of safety by a military amphibious vehicle.

CHAPTER THREE

Hurricane Spotting—Tracking— Warning

One factor that is extremely important to the success of the weather forecaster's activities is a network of swift, extensive communications. Knowing what the meteorological conditions are like some 200 or 300 miles distant from a particular locality can be an enormous help to the weatherman in predicting the weather for his area. This is important enough for reporting normal weather conditions; it becomes vital when storms are involved.

A little over one hundred years ago, when meteorology was just beginning as a specialized field, the weatherman was severely handicapped by the lack of fast communications. Matters had improved somewhat after 1844, the year the telegraph was invented and first put into practical operation between Washington, D.C., and Baltimore, Maryland. Soon thereafter weather experts were able to gather valuable atmospheric data in quick time from widely scattered land points. Later still, wireless came into existence and weather forecasters were able to improve their work further with the help of reports covering vast expanses of land and sea.

A pioneering outgrowth of this technical advance was weather reporting by ships at sea. The first occasion was on December 3, 1905, and soon ship reports became a regular source of information for the weather forecasters. They proved especially helpful when they flashed news about hurricanes, creatures of the tropical seas.

With new and faster methods of communication, the weather reporting service in the United States became better organized. Rec-

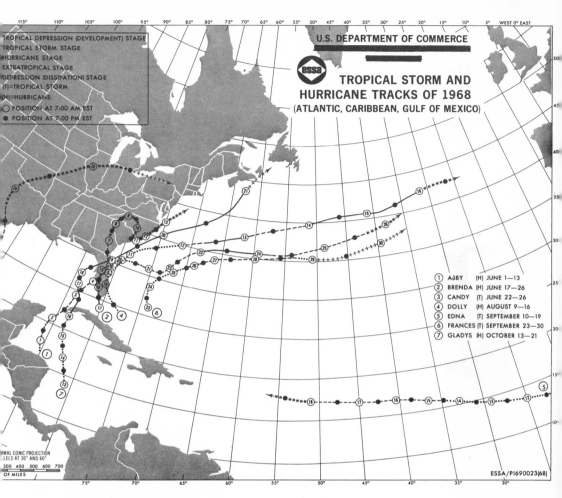

TROPICAL STORM AND HURRICANE TRACKS OF 1968
(ATLANTIC, CARIBBEAN, GULF OF MEXICO)

TROPICAL DEPRESSION (DEVELOPMENT) STAGE
TROPICAL STORM STAGE
HURRICANE STAGE
EXTRATROPICAL STAGE
DEPRESSION (DISSIPATION) STAGE
(T)=TROPICAL STORM
(H)=HURRICANE
○ POSITION AT 7:00 AM EST
● POSITION AT 7:00 PM EST

① ABBY   (H) JUNE 1—13
② BRENDA   (H) JUNE 17—26
③ CANDY   (T) JUNE 22—26
④ DOLLY   (H) AUGUST 9—16
⑤ EDNA   (T) SEPTEMBER 10—19
⑥ FRANCES (T) SEPTEMBER 23—30
⑦ GLADYS   (H) OCTOBER 13—21

RMAL CONIC PROJECTION
.LELS AT 30° AND 60°
300 400 500 600 700
OF MILES

ESSA/PI690023(68)

Tropical Storm and Hurricane Tracks of 1968 (Eastern Hemisphere).

ognizing the value of such a service for the well-being and safety of
the people, particularly in its reporting of storms, the Congress of
the United States in 1870 established a Federal Weather Service.
The group was placed under the management of the U. S. Army
Signal Corps, mainly because this military unit specialized in telegraph communications. Three years later, on August 6, this fledg-
ling weather group passed a historic milestone when it first received
weather reports from the Caribbean Sea area. The news was
flashed from Kingston, Jamaica, and from Havana and Santiago in
Cuba.

Still another historic step was taken by the small weather unit of

51

the U. S. Signal Corps on August 23, 1873, when it issued warnings of a hurricane possibly striking the Atlantic Coast from Cape May, New Jersey, to New London, Connecticut. As matters turned out, the storm fortunately swerved away from the mainland and roared off to sea. In the hurricane season of 1874, the first weather map was published showing the presence of a hurricane.

On October 1, 1880, the United States Congress removed the weather service group from the Signal Corps and established it as

Although the computer has taken over much of the work of preparing weather charts, many are still hand-produced. Such charts are essential for forecasting the weather and for tracking hurricanes.

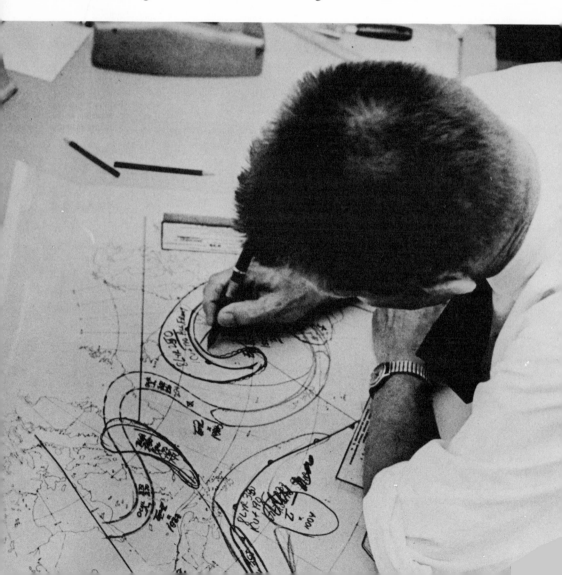

an independent unit, the United States Weather Bureau, within the Department of Agriculture. Much later, in 1940, it became part of the Department of Commerce. The work of the weather experts had expanded and become so vitally important for peacetime, civilian needs that the separation was considered necessary.

In October of 1970 the Weather Bureau was renamed the National Weather Service. It is a key group in the newly organized National Oceanic and Atmospheric Administration (NOAA) within the United States Department of Commerce. The new Administration was created to coordinate the activities that seek a better understanding and use of the air, land, and sea environment of our planet.

The National Weather Service has grown steadily from its pioneer years of the nineteenth century, and the range of its weather observing activities has been greatly extended. Not the least of these is hurricane detection, tracking, and warning. The destruction and enormous toll in human life which these tropical disturbances can visit upon inhabited areas have given the weatherman's attention to these storms the greatest urgency. In order to carry out this phase of the Service's work properly, a large and varied array of tools has slowly been accumulated and adapted for use on the earth's surface, in the atmosphere, and far out into space. The sources of weather information have been forged into a vast network on land, at sea, in the air, and even in outer space.

Because of the special need to detect and warn of the existence of hurricanes, the National Weather Service has established an independent unit, the National Hurricane Center, in Miami, Florida. The men and women weather experts who work at this base have as their sole concern the start and movement of tropical cyclones. As these disturbances approach the mainland of the United States, the Center also issues appropriate warnings to the public. The activities of this hurricane group are carried out the year round. But its busiest time is from the beginning of June to the end of November, the season when hurricanes sweep toward the United States

53

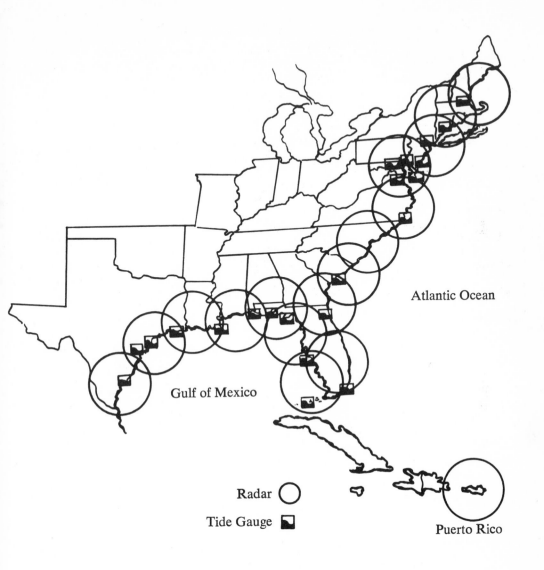

Radar warning network and tide gauges along the Atlantic and Gulf coasts of the United States.
Adapted from *Hurricane*—ESSA, National Oceanic and Atmospheric Administration

Coastal radar stations such as this one are invaluable for spotting and tracking approaching tropical storms.

This is the "storm room" of the National Hurricane Center. Hurricane advisories and warnings are prepared here and then flashed to the public via radio, television, and other communications.

mainland from the southern part of the North Atlantic Ocean, the Caribbean Sea, and the Gulf of Mexico.

All the more familiar weather tools, like the anemometer for checking wind velocity, the barometer, and the thermometer, play key roles in providing weather experts with essential data on which to base their studies and observations. These basic tools are supplemented by countless others including computers, radar, and even cameras aboard satellites spinning around the earth far in space. The data pours into the Center in a steady stream day and night during the hurricane season. Computers help to digest the enormous inflow of information. Weather experts at land stations throughout the West Indies, Mexico, and Central America also contribute thousands of bits of data on weather in their particular areas to the enormous torrent pouring into the Center.

The weather specialists at the Miami Hurricane Center are provided additional data help by the National Meteorological Center near Washington, D. C. The information which this group sends along is a weather summary of the entire Northern Hemisphere. Meteorologists at this base put this together from widely scattered and dissimilar sources of information. These include ships at sea, commercial aircraft on intercontinental flights, and cloud-cover pictures from orbiting weather satellites. Help in putting the Northern Hemisphere weather summary together is also provided by dozens of land weather stations scattered over thousands of square miles.

The use of specially equipped weather satellites, such as the Nimbus and Tiros, to take cloud-cover photographs is one of the latest methods employed by meteorologists for spotting the existence of tropical cyclones. It was in April of 1960 that a twentieth-century space vehicle first accomplished the feat of reporting a cyclone from far out in space. It was Tiros 1, an experimental weather satellite, that recorded the storm while passing over Australia on one of its numerous earthly orbits. When the photos it sent back to earth were analyzed, the outlines of a typhoon with its typical spiraling rain bands were clearly shown, some 800 miles east of Brisbane. The storm's existence was later confirmed by Australian ground weather stations.

In addition to receiving cloud-cover information from the National Environmental Satellite Service, the Miami hurricane base also has direct contact with the picture-taking satellites. This is accomplished with what is called Automatic Picture Transmission (APT). When the weather satellite is within 2,000 miles of a weather station equipped with special receivers, cloud photos

I 2 8   CAMERA

TIROS weather satellite spotting a typhoon over the South Pacific, 1,000 miles east of Australia, April 9, 1960. This was the start of the use of satellites for detecting tropical cyclones.

transmitted by the weather spacecraft can be received automatically. These may number as many as nine a day. Cloud-cover photographs give the Hurricane Center an excellent pictorial view of the tropical regions of the North Atlantic Ocean, the Caribbean Sea, and the Gulf of Mexico, the more common spawning grounds of the hurricane.

Of all the sources of weather information supplied to the Hurricane Center, the most dramatic is surely the Hurricane Hunters. These are weather observers who go on routine air patrols out over the seas in specially equipped aircraft, looking for the start of tropi-

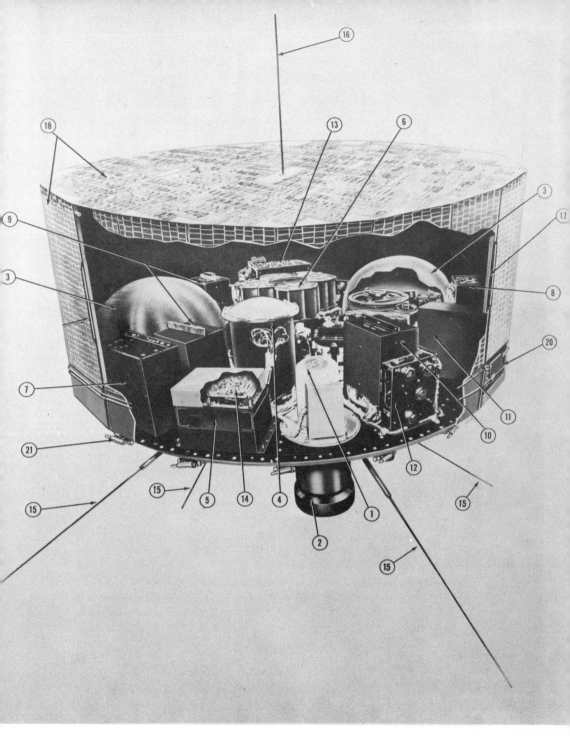

A cutaway view of the TIROS weather satellite. The important equipment includes: (1) one of two cameras, (3) television tape recorders, (5) television transmitter, and (15) transmitting antenna.

TIROS I was the earliest of the working U.S. weather satellites. The light and dark rectangles are solar cells that recharged the satellite's power units.

cal cyclones. If such a disturbance is found, the hurricane spotters not only fly around it to determine the storm's size but also fly into its very center in order to learn how powerful the storm is. Needless to say, this is a highly dangerous assignment. But it is through the bravery of the weathermen who undertake these patrols that so much vitally needed information about hurricanes—size, intensity, path of movement, and much more—is obtained.

The hazardous feat of flying into the vortex of a hurricane was first accomplished by Major Joseph P. Duckworth of the Army Air Corps, on July 23, 1943. Accompanied by Lieutenant Ralph O'Hare, he piloted a small, single-engine military training plane into a storm which was heading for Galveston, Texas. The storm was small but severe. The two men were bounced and tossed hither and yon as they bored through the swirling clouds and winds. Suddenly they broke through the clouds to enter the calm and almost clear eye of the storm. After circling inside this peaceful haven for a few moments, the flyers flew through the maelstrom once again before reaching the safety of an airfield.

When weather forecasters heard of Major Duckworth's feat they shook their heads in disbelief, but were much interested in what the flyers had learned about the storm. To give them the opportunity of finding out for themselves, Major Duckworth went back through

The equipment-filled interior of a Hurricane Hunter patrol plane.

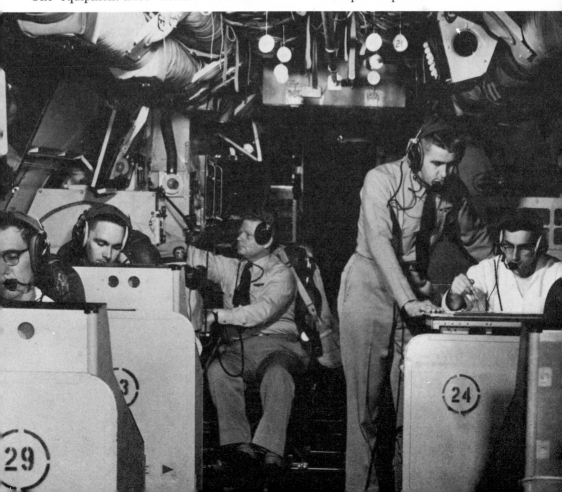

the storm a second time later that day with a trained weather observer as his companion!

As a consequence of this military flyer's pioneering hurricane flight, weather experts were deeply impressed with the valuable help such flights could give in accurately determining the major characteristics of tropical disturbances. Not too long thereafter, in May of 1944, regular air reconnaissance patrols out over the sea were begun by flyers of the Army Air Corps, as the present Air Force was then known, for the purpose of spotting and gathering information on hurricanes. In 1953 the program was taken over and greatly expanded by a squadron of Navy flyers. The daring

Briefing session of a Hurricane Hunter flight crew before take-off.

Weather expert aboard Hurricane Hunter plane plots a storm on a radar-scope.

men assigned to this work were soon given the colorful name, Hurrican Hunters.

Today air patrols for detecting hurricanes are carried out by specially trained crews of Navy and Air Force squadrons. Their efforts are supplemented by civilian pilots working for the National Oceanic and Atmospheric Administration Research Flight Facility. All three groups are at their busiest during the height of the hurricane season.

Hurricane Hunter squadrons carefully comb some 1,500,000 square miles of sea area for budding storms. Flights are made over the Gulf of Mexico, Caribbean Sea, and tropical portions of the Atlantic Ocean. The huge planes, both jets and propeller-driven types, perform low-level missions—500 to 1,000 feet—as well as flights up to 30,000 feet. Most penetrations of hurricanes are made at 10,000 feet.

The Hurricane Hunter planes are crammed with the latest electronic and other equipment adapted for meteorological use. One of the most important items is radar (Radio Detecting And Ranging). Radar came into existence during World War II when it was used for detecting the approach of enemy planes. In the course of this activity it was discovered by chance that it could also clearly indicate the presence of storms. Weather forecasters lost little time in using this electronic eye for storm-spotting purposes thereafter. When a hurricane was first picked up on the viewing scope of a radar unit, the spiraling rain bands were clearly shown, thereby confirming Captain Piddington's pioneering observation on this characteristic of tropical cyclones.

With a single revolution of the radar antenna aboard a Hurricane Hunter plane, 200,000 square miles of ocean area can be monitored. With radar and a complex of other instruments, the weather observers aboard a Hunter plane gather such data as temperature, wind speed and direction, barometric pressure and humidity, quickly relaying it to the Hurricane Center at Miami.

Much of the work of the Hurricane Hunters is routine until a beginning tropical cyclone has been found. The flying weather experts watch it carefully, reporting every change in the storm's intensity and direction of movement. After the storm has reached maturity the airmen begin the dangerous part of their mission by flying directly into the disturbance to determine its size and the velocity of its swirling winds. Sometimes the erratic behavior of a hurricane is such that the storm watchers are called upon to make nighttime flights into the tempests.

As we mentioned earlier, hurricane hunting is a most hazardous activity. Since the establishment of these flying missions more than a quarter of a century ago, there have been some airmen who never returned to their home base after entering a storm. The raging winds proved too great for their aircraft to withstand. The courage and skill of these flyers who calmly enter the powerful whirlwinds of the hurricane cannot be too highly praised or the value of their work too warmly appreciated.

Once a hurricane is detected and its movement carefully observed and plotted, a far-reaching Hurricane Warning Service in the United States goes into operation. The National Hurricane Center at Miami is the major base of activity of the warning system. At this stage of a hurricane's existence the Center not only engages in keeping a close watch on the progress of the storm, but also becomes a clearinghouse for information about the disturbance. This part of the Center's work involves coordinating a steady stream of bulletins and advisories to the public.

The task of properly warning the public about an approaching hurricane is a big responsibility. For greater effectiveness, the

The characteristic spiral pattern of the clouds of a hurricane is clearly shown in this excellent photograph taken from a weather satellite.

Center at Miami shares this job with regional National Weather Service Hurricane Warning offices located at New Orleans, Washington, D.C., Boston, and San Juan, Puerto Rico. Each of these divisional branches has the job of keeping people within an assigned area accurately informed about the hurricane.

The New Orleans office dispenses bulletins and other storm information within a region covering the western and central Gulf coast; the Miami Hurricane Center has jurisdiction over the extreme eastern Gulf region, the western portion of the Caribbean, the Atlantic seaboard south of Cape Hatteras, North Carolina, and the Atlantic Ocean south of latitude 35 degrees north and eastward to the west coasts of Europe and Africa; the Washington, D.C., office has the responsibility for sending out hurricane information to the coastal region north of Cape Hatteras, including New York and Long Island; the Boston office takes care of the New England coastal zone.

Like a lonely sentinel far to the southeast, the National Weather Service office at San Juan, Puerto Rico, is responsible for informing an area covering the eastern Caribbean, and the Atlantic Ocean south of latitude 20 degrees north and between 55 degrees and 75 degrees west longitude.

These divisional weather stations, and other major weather offices in between, along the Gulf and Atlantic coasts, do not neglect their prime function of observing and reporting meteorological conditions. The larger National Weather Service stations from Brownsville, Texas, to Portland, Maine, that are equipped with radar serve as a secondary line of detection and warning. This backup radar fence (each of the electronic eyes has a range of 200 miles) keeps a constant watch for the approach of a storm. The meteorological information gathered by the experts at these secondary observation points is forwarded and added to the avalanche of data pouring into the Hurricane Center at Miami, Florida.

One of the more important pieces of information that the coastal

The hurricane's worst killer comes from the sea. Surge heights along flat coasts can bring catastrophe. The greatest loss of life associated with hurricanes is caused by flooding due to the storm surge. Adequate warning is essential if coastal inhabitants are to escape to safety.

weather stations obtain and pass along relates to the condition of the offshore waters. Hurricanes begin their destructive careers at sea. Their raging winds churn the water into violent, mountainous waves. These race far in advance of the moving disturbances and show their wild presence on the shoreline long before the storm itself arrives.

Tide gauges maintained by the National Ocean Survey (formerly the Coast and Geodetic Survey) stations record the powerful surge of the sea and the towering waves of the surf as the storm draws nearer. This information is relayed to the local weather station where experts analyze and translate the data into predictions as to the time when the surges will arrive and be at their peak. These specialists are also able to tell rather accurately just how destructive the hurricane-driven sea will be.

A swift, extensive communications system for receiving and exchanging storm information links all the National Weather Service stations. The communications arrangement uses the regular message-sending means employed by these stations for their normal activities—teletype and telephone. During the hurricane season, however, a special Hurricane Teletypewriter Circuit is set up and devoted exclusively to storm matters.

The National Weather Service's communications network handling hurricane warnings is also interconnected with other systems operated by such federal government divisions as the Office of Civilian Defense and the armed forces. A further link is maintained with various divisions in local governments dealing with civilian affairs in times of emergency and with private organizations such as the Red Cross. Of course a most important contact is with newspapers and radio and television stations. These provide the general public with up-to-the minute news on the progress of a potentially destructive hurricane.

As a hurricane speeds closer to the mainland, the offices of the National Weather Service issue a series of warnings, each progressively more urgent. The first in this group is a small-craft warning. This is issued when a hurricane moves within a few hundred miles of the coast. Operators of small boats are told to take heed and not go out into the open ocean. The next, more serious, message is a gale warning. When winds are expected to blow at between 38 and 55 miles per hour, a gale warning is added to the small-craft advisory message.

The third of the warning messages is the storm warning. This is sent out when winds are expected in the 55 to 74 miles per hour range. Gale and storm warnings indicate the coastal area to be affected by the warning, the time during which the warning will apply, and the expected intensity of the disturbance. When gale or storm warnings are part of a tropical cyclone advisory, they

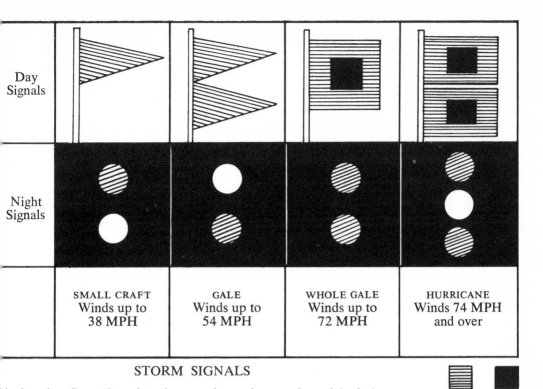

	SMALL CRAFT Winds up to 38 MPH	GALE Winds up to 54 MPH	WHOLE GALE Winds up to 72 MPH	HURRICANE Winds 74 MPH and over

STORM SIGNALS

Displayed at Coast Guard stations, yacht marinas, and municipal piers

Red   Black

may be changed to a hurricane warning if the storm continues along a coast.

The more serious of the storm messages begins with hurricane watch. If a hurricane is known to exist and to be approaching the mainland, threatening coastal and inland regions, a hurricane watch is added to the previous storm advisories. It covers a specific area and the length of time the threat is expected to last. A hurricane watch means that hurricane conditions are a real possibility; it does *not* mean they are about to take place. Everyone in the area covered by the hurricane watch is urged to listen for further advisories and be prepared to act quickly if a hurricane warning should be issued.

A hurricane warning is sent out when hurricane conditions are expected within twenty-four hours. The warning identifies the coastline where winds of at least 74 miles per hour are expected to

blow. A warning may also tell of those coastal areas where dangerously high water or unusually high waves are forecast, even though
winds may be less than hurricane force. A hurricane warning is
seldom issued more than twenty-four hours in advance of an approaching storm. If the hurricane is moving erratically, the warning may be sent out only a few hours before its actual arrival.

In the Pacific adjacent to the continental United States and
around the Hawaiian Islands, the National Weather Service maintains a similar hurricane, or typhoon, warning system. The centers

Global weather patterns are discussed at the National Meteorological Center.

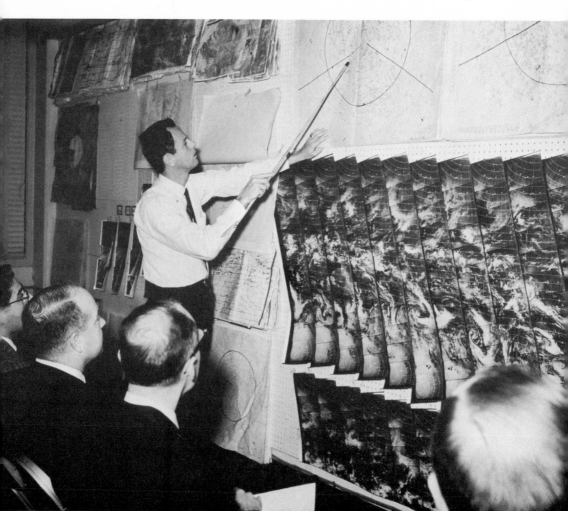

of this activity are at San Francisco and Honolulu. Although tropical cyclone frequency is much greater in the Pacific than in the Atlantic, Caribbean, or Gulf regions, strong easterly winds tend to keep the storms away from the west coast areas and Hawaii. However, in the far west Pacific typhoons do howl with terrific intensity and accomplish vast destruction and many deaths when they veer over land areas. Countries often hit by these devastating storms—the Philippines, Taiwan, China, and Japan—all keep a sharp weather watch once a typhoon is known to be prowling over the Pacific waters.

CHAPTER FOUR

Memorable
Tropical
Cyclones

The West Indies, the lands of Central America fronting on the Gulf of Mexico, and the southern and eastern coasts of the United States have been battered by hurricanes since long before the memory of man. Since the start of meteorological record keeping, super-hurricanes as well as storms of ordinary intensity have been noted. Many of these have lashed the earth with wind and rain of such fierceness that those who experienced the tempests had the feeling the world was in its final death throes.

One of the mightiest of these tropical killer storms was Camille, which roared across the Gulf coast of the United States on August 17, 1969. Before this raging tempest departed from the American continent to disappear out over the Atlantic Ocean, it left 250 people dead, 80 missing, and property damage totaling one and a half billion dollars.

Camille was first spotted on August 5 by a weather satellite near the Cape Verde Islands, which lie off the northwest coast of Africa. The budding storm was nothing more than a huge, mountainous mass of cumulus clouds. Acted upon by the warm, moist air of the tropical seas, the disturbance slowly grew in size and eventually became a full-blown hurricane. Caught in the prevailing trade winds, the storm traveled westward across the southern part of the Atlantic Ocean.

Experts at the Hurricane Center in Miami recognized the symptoms of a hurricane presented in the satellite photos. They watched the disturbance carefully and became more certain of its

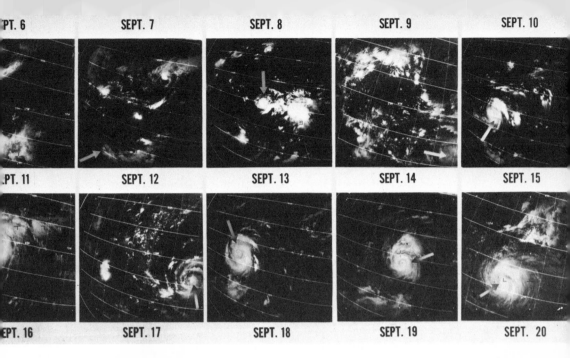

Weather satellites have become valuable tools for spotting and tracking tropical cyclones. This series of photos shows Hurricane Beulah being watched by a weather satellite from the beginning stage of the storm to its full growth in September of 1967.

character when additional pictures were flashed earthward by the weather eye in space. By August 12 there was no longer any question that the tropical disturbance was an intense hurricane. It was now slashing parts of Puerto Rico and growing increasingly violent.

The following day, August 13, the cyclone was nearing Cuba. At this point the disturbance began acting in a strange manner. Forecasters thought it was separating into two storms. Hurricane Hunter planes were sent out to investigate. One of the aircraft explored the region north of Cuba but found nothing. Another Hunter plane flew south and located the storm's center raging full-blast off Grand Cayman Island, south of Cuba.

Now that the true center of the storm was located, Hurricane Hunter planes based at Puerto Rico flew repeatedly into the heart of the tempest. The information which the flying weathermen found caused a great deal of eyebrow raising among the experts. The storm's center indicated a near record-breaking barometric reading of 26.61 inches. The fiercely spiraling winds were unbelievable—estimated as high as 190 miles per hour.

Camille was a tropical cyclone of mighty proportions and power. Now the hurricane forecasters were faced with the most difficult part of their work, tracking the movement of the disturbance. Like many sister storms of the past, Camille took a curving northwestward path through the Gulf, skirting the western tip of Cuba.

Hurricane Camille, with winds over 200 m.p.h., was the most destructive to hit the continental United States. This aerial view shows some of the extensive damage the storm caused near Mobile, Alabama.

Timely warnings to weather stations in that country saved many people from injury and death. The big question was where the storm would head after moving away from the vicinity of Cuba.

Every piece of data the storm experts had that gave a clue to the ultimate direction of the hurricane was fed into a computer. After digesting the mass of information, the electronic brain told the weathermen that the storm in all likelihood would strike the southern section of Florida, traveling in a northeast direction. The prediction was received with some skepticism by many of the forecasters. Basing their doubts on the behavior of past storms, as well as on other meteorological data with which they were working, their feeling was that the cyclone was more apt to zero in on the northwest corner of Florida instead. This was the decision finally agreed to by the experts at the Hurricane Center and accordingly a hurricane watch was sent out on the morning of August 16, covering an area from St. Marks, Florida, to Biloxi, Mississippi.

Early the next day the erratic nature of Camille became all too clear, and forecasters were almost at a loss as to where the storm would really strike. Because of the perplexing movement of the storm, the hurricane warnings were extended farther west to New Orleans, Louisiana, as a precaution. While off the west Florida coast and playing tag with the weather experts, Camille refueled from the warm Gulf waters and acquired more ferocity than ever.

By 10:30 A.M. on Sunday, August 17, it was almost a certainty that Camille was going to avoid the Florida coast and smash inland somewhere between Mississippi and Louisiana. People in many of the communities facing the Gulf in those states took heed of the warnings that were flowing in a steady stream from the radio and television stations. They packed whatever they could of their more precious belongings in family cars and drove to interior areas for safety. They were wise. Others who chose to ignore the warnings paid dearly, many with their lives.

As darkness fell on that memorable Sunday, there was no longer

75

This Gulfport, Mississippi, house was one of thousands leveled by Hurricane Camille, which struck the Gulf Coast of the United States in August of 1969.

any doubt as to where Camille was headed. The storm slammed inland with its center just west of the city of Gulfport, Mississippi. Its winds were shrieking at an estimated 190 miles per hour. The rain falling from its swirling clouds was a veritable deluge. The hurricane-force winds of the storm extended for 175 miles. Scores of communities in a 600-square-mile area that took the full measure of Camille's angry blows were soon without light and power. Darkness added to the frightening aspects of the storm.

During the period of the storm's full intensity, people were urged to stay where they were and not try to escape along the highways. Roads had become impassable with fallen trees, broken utility poles, and dangling power lines. The debris of houses transformed into kindling wood by Camille's winds added to the obstructions.

Homes and other buildings nearest the water were hardest hit. What Camille's raging winds did not rip loose and splinter, huge tidal surges of water from the Gulf finished. An awesome wall of water 25 feet high was the climax of this part of Camille's activity.

76

The giant tides and waves not only swept structures out of their path but took many lives in the process. There was no doubt in the minds of those who weathered the storm or the experts who tried so desperately to gauge its behavior and track its movement that Camille was a tropical cyclone of immense ferocity. Dr. Robert H. Simpson, head of the Hurricane Center at Miami, described it as "the greatest recorded storm ever to hit a heavily populated area of the Western Hemisphere."

Although the death and destruction in the Gulf coast region was enormous, Camille had not yet spent her anger. Continuing her journey northward the next several days, Camille no longer carried her devastating winds but did bring disturbed weather, clouds,

This aerial photo shows part of Biloxi, Mississippi, devastated by Hurricane Camille in 1969. Camille was responsible for the death of more than 250 people and $1.5 billion in property damage.

strong winds and rain, wherever she appeared. The storm moved through Tennessee and Kentucky, then, still unpredictable, swung sharply eastward through Virginia.

For reasons not quite clear to meteorologists, Camille had either conserved some of her original cargo of rain or had in some manner acquired fresh quantities. In the span of six hours the storm dumped almost 30 inches of rain over approximately 3,000 square miles of Virginia terrain. The torrential rains caused rivers to rise quickly, overflow their banks, and flood surrounding areas. Hillsides became sliding avalanches of mud, crushing houses and other structures in their paths. When Camille finally swept out to sea, scores of people had lost their lives, most of them drowning in the overflowing and wildly surging river waters.

As a result of its enormous destructiveness, first as a hurricane and then as a deluge, Camille was responsible for the deaths of 330 people. Although the experience showed how much more knowledge forecasters need, the better to judge the intensity and movement of these storms, nevertheless the warnings they were able to issue with respect to Camille undoubtedly saved the lives of many more hundreds of potential victims.

Measured against other hurricanes of the past, Camille was a mighty storm. Yet there have been storms that brought death to people on a much larger scale both in the United States and in those parts of the world where tropical cyclones are common. In 1900 Galveston, Texas, was struck a mighty blow by a hurricane that caused almost the entire city to disappear under the waters of the Gulf of Mexico. The wind-driven seas drowned an estimated 6,000 of the city's inhabitants. On September 2, 1935, a roaring hurricane that smashed over the Florida Keys left 400 dead in its wake. Many of the victims were World War I veterans stationed at a work camp on one of the Keys.

As the storm reached its peak it was realized by emergency workers that the camp and its occupants were exposed and in grave danger of being swept into the sea. Not only were fierce

Disbelief shows on the face of a little boy viewing the wreckage of his home after Hurricane Camille passed by.

winds tearing everything apart above surface, but mountainous seas were rolling in over the low-lying land. A train was dispatched to rescue the veterans. Unfortunately, it never reached its destination. With the exception of the engine, the cars of the train were thrown off the tracks by the powerful, rolling seas as though they were toys.

It was in the course of this storm that meteorologists recorded the lowest barometric reading in the Western Hemisphere, 26.35 inches.

Another memorable hurricane with much the same brute power

as the Keys storm smashed across Long Island and into southern New England, on September 21, 1938. Like Camille, this storm was thought by weather experts to have had its start near the Cape Verde Islands. In those days meteorologists did not have the technologically advanced tools and electronic devices for detecting and tracking these tropical cyclones that they use today—as, for example, weather satellites.

The full-blown hurricane roared northward along the Atlantic coast, then tore into Long Island with winds raging between 125 and 150 miles per hour. The center and most powerful part of the storm struck near the eastern end of Long Island. The loss of life and destruction were appalling. Houses and other structures along

A powerful hurricane swept up the Atlantic Coast in September of 1938, slashed across Long Island and deep into New England, leaving an enormous trail of death and destruction. Photo shows some of the damage caused by the storm's high winds at Montauk, Long Island.

the south shore were smashed into splinters and swept away by a booming, gigantic surf. Trees in countless numbers were knocked down, along with electric power and telephone lines. Boats in bays and creeks, thought by their owners to be securely tied against the power of the storm, were torn loose from their moorings, lifted by waves and wind, and deposited in places far inland.

After killing scores of people and leaving much of Long Island in shambles, the storm raced across Long Island Sound to crash full-tilt into southern New England. Here the rampaging hurricane repeated its destructive ways. When the tempest finally blew itself to sea, it had killed approximately 600 people and destroyed property in the neighborhood of 300 million dollars.

Curving in a long arc from near the southern tip of Florida to the northern edge of South America, the West Indies lie across the path of most of the hurricanes that have swept out of the southern portion of the northern Atlantic Ocean. Since time immemorial they have borne shattering blows from countless tropical cyclones. Typical of these was the storm of October 10, 1780, rarely equaled for its death-dealing blows and devastation.

An early eye-witness account of the great storm tells of its first arrival over the island of Barbados where almost all the trees and houses were leveled to the ground. The same tempest sank a British fleet anchored in a bay at the Island of St. Lucia and killed close to 6,000 of the island's inhabitants.

Continuing on its destructive path, this tropical cyclone tore into the island of Martinique. A French convoy of more than 40 ships with 4,000 soldiers aboard was sent to the bottom with all hands. Twice that number of civilians on the island were killed. The storm eventually boomed its way northward to Bermuda where its last activities were reported. Even at that distance from where it had originated and despite the fact that its power had diminished, the storm was still strong enough to sink several ships.

Deadly tropical cyclones spawned in the Bay of Bengal and the Indian Ocean from time to time slash populated areas along the

81

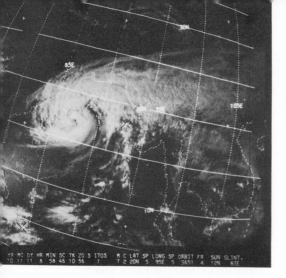
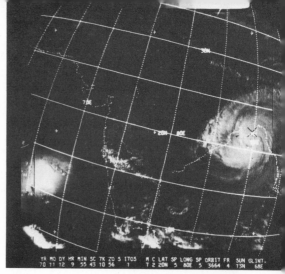

One of the most devastating tropical cyclones in history roared out of the Bay of Bengal in November of 1970, struck the low-lying coastal area of East Pakistan, and killed an estimated 190,000 people. Most of the victims drowned in huge tidal waves. These photos of the storm were taken by the United States weather satellite ITOS-I.

southern edge of India's coast. A monstrous killer storm appeared in this region in 1737, roaring inland at the mouth of the Hooghly River, near Calcutta. It rolled enormous storm waves, 40 feet high, over shore areas having densely populated settlements. After the storm winds and waters had subsided, 300,000 Indians were estimated to have been drowned. More than a hundred years later, in 1864, a cyclone of almost equal ferocity smashed into the same area, this time taking 50,000 people to their deaths.

A modern disaster of similar proportions took place in November of 1970, striking the offshore islands and low-lying coast of East Pakistan. A tropical cyclone originating over the Bay of Bengal lashed the seas into giant waves. These surged over the islands and coastline, continuing far inland. The precise number of people killed was never determined but the estimate was placed at 191,000.

Pacific typhoons are equally notorious for their tremendous power and the death and destruction which they are capable of dealing out. People of the Philippines, the South China coast, and

Japan, where typhoons often hit, know all too well the punishment these weather disturbances can deliver. One of the most memorable of these storms occurred in 1944, at the height of the Pacific naval action in World War II.

Following the disaster of Pearl Harbor, United States land and sea forces slowly pushed the Japanese back across the Pacific, from one island to another. By December of 1944, General Douglas MacArthur and Admiral William Halsey were ready to deliver a one-two blow against the Japanese forces on the Philippines, one of the last of their strongholds.

In preparation for the mass onslaught and invasion, Admiral Halsey had met the Japanese fleet and dealt it a crippling attack in Leyte Gulf. Now the American naval officer was regrouping his Third Fleet, one of the most powerful naval armadas in all history, for another attack and landing at Luzon, in the Philippines. An essential part of the regrouping activity was the refueling of the warships. This operation was to be carried out several hundred miles east of Luzon, where oil tankers and ships of the Third Fleet were to rendezvous. At the start of this rather difficult operation nature intervened with a howling typhoon.

The first menacing signs of the storm appeared on December 17, with the sea and wind rapidly increasing in force. Seamen aboard battleships, aircraft carriers, destroyers, and other vessels of the armada were finding it harder and harder to keep oil hoses and mooring lines from breaking away from the tankers. Time after time the hoses pulled clear and the lines broke as the seas surged higher and grew more violent. Over all hung the greater danger that the ships would crash into one another.

By evening it was clear to seamen and officers alike that they were in the grip of a roaring typhoon, and refueling was ordered stopped. Survival was uppermost now as the ships of the fleet sought to escape the fury of the storm. The sea was whipped into writhing mountains. The ships struggled up the sloping walls of water, poised momentarily on the crests, then plunged crazily down

A United States Navy aircraft carrier listing sharply during a typhoon in the South China Sea, December 17, 1944.

the sides almost completely buried under tons of water. It was impossible to tell where sea and sky met. All was a furious, churning world of water.

Radio operators remained glued to their posts, striving to pick up weather information from more distant points—any place to which the ships might go to escape the fury of the tempest. Navigators worked feverishly over their charts, plotting new directions for the battered fleet. Through the night of December 17 the typhoon grew progressively worse, although those in it did not think it could. Ships were being battered into a state of helplessness. There was no longer any effort to keep the fleet together as a unit. Every vessel was on its own, fighting for its existence.

Tremendous seas pounded stacks, antennas, lifeboats, and all sorts of exposed equipment on the ships' decks into useless wreckage or swept it overboard. The smaller vessels, destroyers, escort

84

boats and others suffered the most. Their lack of fuel made them light as corks, causing them to pitch violently fore and aft and to roll wildly from side to side. They were in the greatest danger of going under. On the eighteenth, still in the coils of the typhoon, the Third Fleet was a shattered armada. Many of the warships were no longer fighting machines but helpless hulks, rolling out of control and at the mercy of raging winds and seas.

When the nightmare finally ended and the scattered warships were together again, a survey showed the casualties and damage to be enormous. Three destroyers had been rolled over by the giant waves and sent to the bottom. From these and other vessels, about 1,000 men were drowned. Aircraft carriers had flight decks buckled, while battleships, cruisers, and destroyers all received equally serious damage. More than 150 aircraft had been blown from the ships as though they were toy models. The storm-ravaged Third Fleet was in such a bad state that any idea of pursuing the plan

The bow of this U. S. Navy destroyer is almost completely buried under rough seas during a typhoon in the South China Sea, in December of 1944.

for attacking at Luzon had to be abandoned. Weeks passed before the American fleet recovered from its battering by the monster typhoon.

To help make the task of tracking hurricanes or typhoons easier, a variety of means have been suggested and used. In the 1800's weather observers in the West Indies tagged these storms with the names of saints on whose days the hurricanes struck. Weathermen in the United States for a brief period identified tropical storms with letters of the alphabet. Hurricanes were listed as A-1943, B-1943, and so forth.

In World War II, weather forecasters employed a different and more widely used system based on the phonetic alphabet. Tropical cyclones were then best known as Able, Baker, Charlie, and others following in alphabetical sequence. But this was not quite satisfactory to weather experts and they kept looking for other methods of identification.

New ways have been suggested for naming storms—after animals, famous personalities, places, or even mythological figures. In Australia weather observers tagged typhoons with the names of unpopular political figures!

The current system of weather experts in the United States is to give hurricanes the names of girls. The first published usage of a girl's name to identify a violent storm is believed to have appeared in 1941 in a novel, *Storm*, written by George Stewart. About the same time weather forecasters, newspaper reporters, and radio announcers for some unknown reason were beginning to refer to tropical storms as "she." This was much like the custom of talking about ships as "she." At any rate the practice caught on and grew in popularity. After some years of use the United States National Weather Service made it official in 1953.

The National Weather Service now employs a semipermanent list of four sets of girls' names for identifying tropical cyclones which are listed alphabetically and used in regular sequence as

Sailors struggle ashore from their ship stricken off the coast of Rhode Island by Hurricane Donna.

each storm makes an appearance. Almost two dozen names make up a list for a single season. Some charming identifications for these violent ladies include: Alma, Blanche, Camille, Martha, and Rhoda. Names that start with Q, U, X, Y, and Z are not used because there are so few of them.

A separate set of names is started each year at the beginning of the hurricane season. The sets of names are rotated every four years. The names of exceptionally powerful hurricanes, like Betsy of 1965 and Camille of 1969, are retired permanently. Other names are substituted. Typhoons and hurricanes in the Pacific are also given feminine names.

Anyone who has gone through a hurricane is not likely soon to forget the experience. The fury of these storms is awesome and, of course, dangerous. Because of the great likelihood of death and destruction which these tempests can bring to any area, precautions are always urged for those places where hurricanes are frequent visitors. The Gulf coast of the United States and the Florida peninsula are two regions where at least one or more tropical cyclones can be expected every season.

At the beginning of every hurricane period in the United States, the National Weather Service sends out a series of safety instructions for people who live in storm-threatened localities. For example, those inhabiting low-lying areas close to the water should move to higher ground. More deaths occur by drowning due to sea surges than by hurricane-wind destruction. People who have boats are urged to take them to sheltered places farther inland. If this is not possible then the least to be done is to see that the boats are firmly moored.

Windows of houses and business structures should be boarded, or storm shutters put in place if they are available. Wind pressure and flying debris are the two main causes of broken windows. Loose objects outdoors around the home should be firmly anchored or put into storage, so as not to be blown away by the wind. Drinking water should be stored in clean bathtubs, jugs, bottles, and cooking utensils as a precaution against the possibility that the public water supply may become contaminated by flood waters. Since it is almost a certainty that the electric power of a storm-struck locality will be knocked out, emergency cooking and lighting facilities should be prepared. These measures might include putting fresh batteries in flashlights and battery-operated radios, replenishing the oil in oil lamps, and having a fresh supply of candles on hand. An alcohol burner for cooking might also be made ready.

Finally, the National Weather Service urges that all persons who are experiencing a hurricane should be alert to happenings during the course of the storm. The radio should be kept operating for the latest hurricane information. By following these simple instructions and exercising common sense, most people who go through a hurricane will have experienced nothing more than a dramatic event.

CHAPTER FIVE

"Tornado!"

"Tornado!" This warning cry is enough to send a chill down the spine of the bravest. And for good reason. The tornado is the most destructive and vicious of all storms. Although a great deal smaller than the hurricane, the giant of all weather disturbances, the tornado can perform its work of destruction and death in a far more complete fashion and a great deal faster.

Like the hurricane, the tornado belongs to the cyclone family of storms. It too has winds that spin in a whirlpool fashion. In areas of the United States where tornadoes are common, people also often refer to them as "twisters."

Tornadoes occur throughout the world. But the one place where they seemingly strike with the most frequency is in central United

The first photo ever taken of a tornado, about 1880.

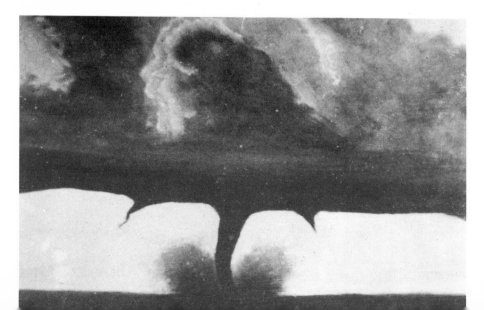

The destruction of a battlefield could hardly be greater than that caused by a tornado. This is a part of Lubbock, Texas, devastated by a tornado in May of 1970.

States, between the Rocky Mountains and the Appalachians. All fifty states of this nation, however, can expect to receive blows from this devastating storm. Weather experts in the United States have found through studying tornadoes over a period of years that the season when they appear all too frequently is April, May, and June. The time when they occur least is in December and January.

No other storm that sweeps the earth's surface is quite like the tornado. It is a frightening spectacle that is made more so by dark, swirling thunderstorm clouds from which it usually springs. The most unique part of the tornado is the long, sinuous, funnel-shaped cloud that dangles toward the earth from the black cumulonimbus storm clouds. This eerie funnel cloud, swaying this way and that from the blackened sky, is actually a vortex of winds whirling in a counterclockwise direction at tremendous speed. No one has ever measured exactly the velocity of these whirling winds because of the extreme danger of their power. Nevertheless, a good estimate has been arrived at based on the degree of damage the winds have achieved. It is believed that the winds easily reach a speed of 300 miles per hour and perhaps more.

The extremely rapid spinning of the winds of the vortex causes them to condense to form a light-colored cloud. This is the visible part of the tornado that can be most frightening to observers. The interior of this funnel-shaped cloud is hollow. A partial vacuum

This aerial view shows the splintered remains of homes in Lubbock, Texas, blasted by the tornado in May 1970.

exists inside the funnel, caused by the mechanical energy, centrifugal force, produced by the rapidly rotating winds. When spinning at their maximum speed, these whirling winds have enormous lifting power in their upward, vertical path.

Sometimes the writhing, pendulous tornado cloud will simply dangle from the storm clouds and not touch the ground, but in most cases it does. When this happens, devastation starts. Anything over which the funnel may drape itself is almost certain to be blasted into a total wreck. Only the most substantial steel and concrete structures are capable of remaining upright. And even these are likely to suffer some damage.

In those instances where the tornado cloud will keep its bottom end to the earth's surface, it will cut a path of unbelievable destruction about a quarter of a mile wide and 16 miles long on the average. But the movement of a tornado, like that of most storms, is unpredictable. Some funnels will never touch the ground, while others will remain earth-bound until they die away. There is still a third type that will tantalize areas by dipping and rising over a

This dramatic photo shows the awesome funnel shape of the dreaded tornado.

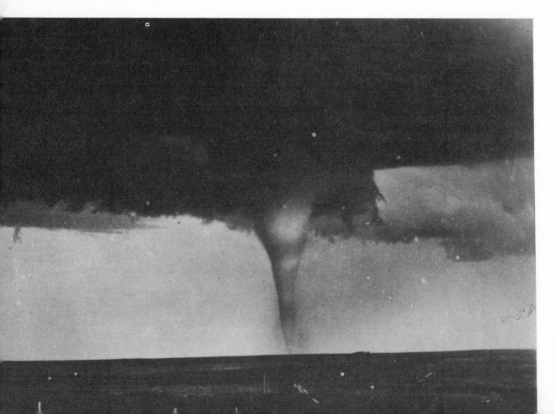

A once comfortable home was transformed into kindling wood after the passage of a tornado through Jonesboro, Arkansas, in May 1968.

long stretch. The result is a weird pattern of destroyed and untouched areas.

When the end of the tornado funnel touches the ground, the devastation period of the storm begins. The debris of objects caught within its vortex is whirled upward. This and dust from the earth frequently darken the whirlwind cloud, adding to its ominous appearance.

If it were possible to watch a tornado in action from a safe vantage point, it would seem that an area where its funnel touched was under violent artillery bombardment. Wreckage flies in all directions. The partial vacuum of the funnel's interior is a destroyer

Tornadoes sometimes spawn twin funnels, as shown in this photo taken near Elkhart, Indiana.

equally as powerful as the storm's winds. The vacuum causes a sharp drop in atmospheric pressure and has an explosive effect on any structure the funnel happens to touch. Windows and walls of houses are easily blown out by this feature of tornadoes. Rooftops are frequently sent flying.

The combined destructive power of a tornado's winds and vacuum can make kindling out of wooden building in the twinkling of an eye. Even structures of steel and brick, if not properly built, can be totally wrecked by the tornado's fierce power.

Although a single funnel-shaped tornado cloud is more apt to occur from a thunderstorm, this is not always the case. There have been instances when two and more funnels have been spawned by a single storm. These may not only swing and sway over the earth's surface to carry out multiple destruction, they may also

94

come and go in rapid sequence after traveling for only a few miles. Since they are part of and attached to thunderstorm clouds, tornadoes generally move forward at a speed related to that of the parent storm. Their forward velocity can range anywhere from zero to a maximum speed of approximately 70 miles per hour.

Most tornadoes that extend downward from thunderstorm clouds have funnel-shaped clouds. They are broad at the top where they are attached to the cumulonimbus thunderclouds and narrow at the end touching the earth. However, not all have this shape. Some clouds are more like a column, straight up and down. Another kind, although far from common according to the experts, is shaped like an hourglass, broad at the top and bottom and narrow in the middle. These unusual funnels of the tornado are shaped for the most part by the winds of the thunderstorm.

As if the visible aspects of the pendant tornado cloud were not sufficiently frightening, there is also a roaring noise when the end of the funnel strikes the earth. Those who have safely gone through the nerve-racking experience of a tornado have stretched their imaginations to find some comparable sound to describe that created by a "twister." Some have likened the tornado noise to that of a thousand railroad cars rattling over a crossing. Others have felt that the noise is more like the prolonged sound of bombardment from a thousand cannons. Perhaps the most unusual of the comparisons describes the tornado's noise as a kind of whirring sound similar to that generated by the buzzing of a million bees. Whatever the tornado noise may be compared with, there is no question but that this characteristic of the storm adds greatly to its frightfulness.

Meteorologists know a great deal about tornadoes, especially the atmospheric conditions necessary for spawning the "twisters." What they do not know precisely is how all the disturbed or differing atmospheric factors interact one with another to bring a tornado into existence. Many theories have been advanced but all in some measure fail to meet the scientific need for absolute certainty.

The over-all atmospheric disturbances that bring tornadoes into existence are those that create the common thunderstorm. These include radical temperature differences and contrasts in air density and moisture content. The necessary dissimilar atmospheric characteristics are brought about by a collision between cool and warm air masses. The interaction of the two creates a weather front, a kind of meteorological battleground.

The visible signs of the tug-of-war taking place along a weather front include a variety of cloud formations, usually in a rapid state of movement; strong, gusty winds; thunderstorms; rain or snow. It is out of this atmopheric turbulence that tornadoes are most likely to spring.

Incidentally, the reason these extremely violent, devastating

Visual data such as this flashed to earth by orbiting weather satellites help in forecasting tornadoes. The cloud structure shown extended over parts of Michigan, Kentucky, and Ohio and produced several killer tornadoes.

A "twister" passing through Enid, Oklahoma, in 1966.

storms seem to favor the central plains of the United States is due to the fact that the region is a meeting place for cool air masses from the north and warm air masses from the south. Since the collision of the two dissimilar air masses takes place at altitudes ranging from one-half mile to a mile, mountains would provide obstacles to such meetings. On the wide open plains there are no such terrain barriers to interfere with the movements of the air masses.

In the winter season struggles between cool and warm air masses are few because the former is more or less in prolonged command. When spring and early summer arrive, matters change drastically. The presence of warm air masses from the south becomes more frequent and lasting. It aggressively forces the cool air mass to retreat north. The weather at this period becomes highly disturbed in

The explosive, ripping force of a tornado made kindling wood of this home and a splintered wreck of the tree.

the region where the two meet. Thus, as mentioned earlier, the plains of the central United States can expect more tornadoes in April, May, and June than at any other time of the year.

Weather scientists do not lack for ideas as to how tornadoes are triggered from thunderstorms. There are two rather popular theories at the moment. One is based on thermal (heat) forces and the other on mechanical forces. Those supporting the thermal concept believe that the tornado is born when the atmosphere is thrown radically out of balance when a cool air mass overcomes a warm air mass. Nature tries to create an equalizing force with swift upward currents of warm air. The rapidity and strength of these vertically rising air currents tend to shape them into a rotating flow. This fast-rising, spinning air flow eventually becomes the vortex of the tornado.

Scientists who advance the mechanical force theory think the tornado's whirlwinds begin in the meeting of two air currents already in a state of rotation because of atmospheric disturbances. The many factors in the latter category are created by the collision of two differing air masses.

The initial spinning of the converging winds is restricted and even the area of their rotation made smaller by other atmospheric forces. As the path or radius is made constantly smaller, the speed of the rotating winds becomes faster. This is likened to the action of a figure skater who, in order to increase his spinning speed, will draw his arms closer to his body. The whirling winds in time will attain such a velocity as to become the start of the tornado vortex.

Other meteorologists who make tornadoes their special field of study are more inclined to the idea that it is a combination of the above two theories that produces tornadoes. Although both thermal and mechanical forces are involved, according to this line of

MECHANICAL THEORY OF
TORNADO FORMATION

THERMAL THEORY OF
TORNADO FORMATION

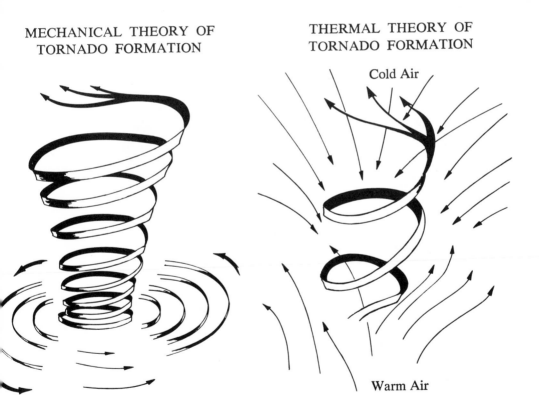

Adapted from *Tornado*—ESSA, National Oceanic and Atmospheric Administration

thought, one or the other eventually will dominate to create and develop the tornado's whirlwinds.

Tornadoes, the offspring of thunderstorms, tend to inherit one deadly characteristic of their parent storm—lightning. Quick, dazzling electrical discharges are a common feature of tornadoes. These occur both within and around the outside of the dangling, swaying funnel-shaped cloud. It was a rare, chance view by a lucky observer into the interior of a tornado funnel as it passed overhead that provided information on the electrical activity that takes place there. The lightning strokes were reported so swift and numerous as to create a blue glow inside the funnel.

Because of lightning's association with tornadoes, some scientists believe this electrical force may be a major energy source that gives speed and power to the tornado's rotating winds. On the other hand, there is a group of weather experts who take a completely

The frightening approach of a "twister."

opposite view. Their idea is that the tremendous speed of the storm's whirling winds is actually the source for the numerous lightning flashes.

All the current theories on how tornadoes start are interesting. However, the problem faced by the experts is to find convincing evidence to support their beliefs. This is proving an elusive and difficult task. Not the least of the reasons for this are the highly dangerous nature of tornadoes, their unpredictability, and the near impossibility of subjecting such storms to scientific investigation.

Despite those handicaps, weather scientists in the United States are pushing their research activities with a good deal of vigor. They have two main incentives. One is the objective of gaining knowledge for the sake of pure science. The other is the hope that by obtaining a clearer understanding of the origin and nature of tornadoes they will be better able to predict the arrival of these brief but intense storms. This in turn would enable them to give improved advance warnings to the public and thus reduce the loss of life.

Tornadoes take place over water as well as over land. When they occur at sea, the funnel-shaped weather disturbances are called waterspouts. They are shaped just like land tornadoes, but their vortex does not have the same degree of power. In size they are also much the same as their land cousins. The forward speed of a moving waterspout can range from almost nothing to about 40 miles per hour.

To observers at sea, a waterspout can be just as awesome a sight as is the land-based tornado. This is especially true for those "twisters" that reach their average maximum height of a mile. Even though waterspouts may not be as powerful as tornadoes, they are not taken lightly by seamen. When possible, ships are maneuvered out of the way of these sea-born "twisters." Large ships as a rule are not as vulnerable to waterspouts as are small craft. If caught in the vortex, the latter can be capsized or badly damaged. Sometimes fish swimming near the surface of the sea will

be sucked up by the waterspout's whirling winds, carried a considerable distance, and then deposited on land.

In regions with numerous lakes or where the terrain is cut by a river and its branches, "twisters" have been known to change from tornadoes to waterspouts and back to tornadoes as the funnel moved successively over land and water.

While the normal life-span of a tornado is comparatively short, measured in minutes, and its path of travel not very wide or long, there have been a number of exceptional performers. One of these made its appearance on May 26, 1917, doing its dance of death and destruction across Illinois and Indiana for a distance of 293 miles. The tornado completed its journey after 7 hours and 20 minutes. The killer storm moved along at a speed of 40 miles an hour, about the average for "twisters."

Tornadoes can strike the same place more than once. Although the chance of any one locality's being hit is extremely small, even for those in the so-called tornado belt in midwestern United States, there have been numerous occasions when communities have been dealt recurring blows by these powerful storms. Working out a table of probabilities, weather scientists say that for the most dangerous area in the nation, the possibility that a particular locality will be hit by a tornado is about once in 250 years. This reassuring outlook exists even though statistics show that on the average, the United States is struck by more than 620 tornadoes a year.

Oklahoma City seems to be one of the favorite targets of tornadoes. Since 1892, this thriving community has been hit twenty-six times. An even more dramatic example is furnished by the town of Baldwyn, Mississippi, which was struck twice by tornadoes within a period of twenty-five minutes on March 16, 1942. Other areas that have suffered multiple visits include Irving, Kansas,

This interesting photo shows the circular scars in an Iowa cornfield left by the powerful swirling winds of a tornado that passed over the area in May of 1968.

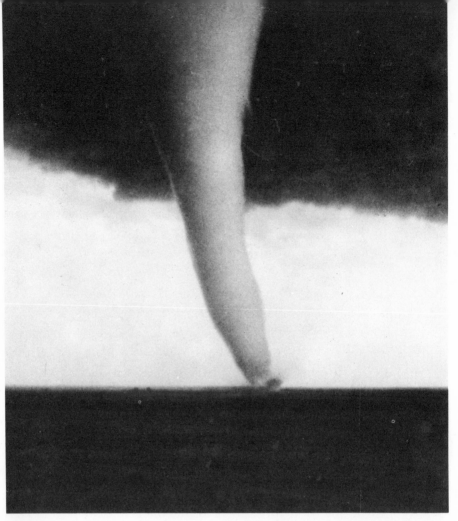

which was almost completely demolished by two tornadoes that smashed into the community within 45 minutes of each other. Austin, Texas, the state capital, was also ripped by two quick visiting tornadoes on May 4, 1922.

While there are a number of unpredictable features about tornadoes, there is nothing uncertain about the degree of destruction that they can accomplish. As described earlier, the combination of the "twister's" tremendous winds and the vacuum effect of the funnel-shaped cloud's interior can reduce a community to complete rubble in a matter of minutes. And there have been countless examples of the extraordinary power of these storms.

The tornado's winds and explosive power can rip and blast the most solid of buildings into a near total wreck. The debris that it creates out of the destroyed structures is converted into a barrage of deadly missiles that kill and maim. The tornado's power is also of such a unique nature that it can take a straw and drive it end foremost into a wooden object, much as a needle is pushed into soft, yielding material. Similarly, large hunks of wood have been blown end first into tree trunks and the walls of buildings without breaking.

Close-up of a wood fragment torn loose by tornado winds and driven into a section of a steel gatepost, striking evidence of the power of these storms.

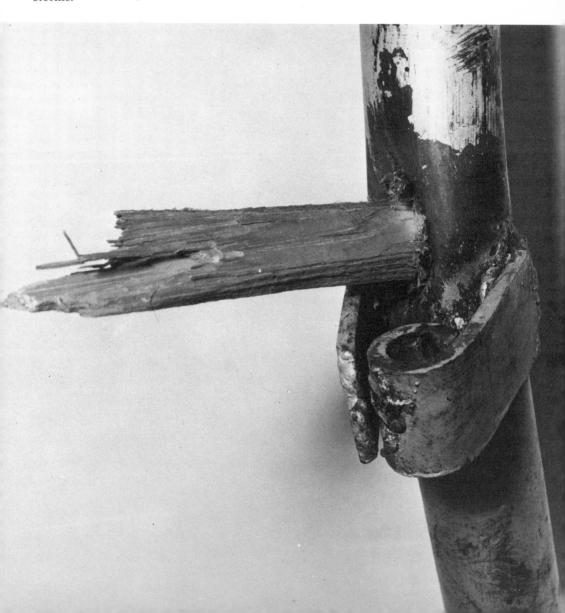

Giant trees have been torn from the ground as though they were weeds and tossed far from their original spot. People, horses, cattle, among other animals, have also been lifted bodily from the earth by the whirling winds and thrown hundreds of feet away, usually with fatal results. A tornado of unusual power struck a portion of Minnesota in 1931. It performed the herculean feat of lifting a railroad coach weighing 83 tons and its 117 passengers completely off the tracks. The coach and passengers were blown 80 feet through the air before being dropped into a ditch. Tornadoes handle automobiles as if they were toys. They can lift these vehicles into the air, toss them about wildly, then smash the cars back to earth into heaps of scrap. The fantastic stories of a tornado's enormous power are endless.

The property damage that can be achieved by a tornado may be unbelievable in the degree of destruction. But the human loss, in death and injuries, after a "twister" has passed through a community is quite another matter and certainly the most serious aspect of visits by these storms. The death toll in the United States alone from tornadoes averages more than 120 a year. The injured number in the thousands. Perhaps the worst tornado "epidemic" on record to strike the midwestern United States occurred on Palm Sunday, April 11, 1965. An amazing total of 37 tornadoes formed from the warm, humid thunderstorm conditions that prevailed over a wide area. Before the day ended the deadly "twisters" had killed 271 people, injured more than 5,000, and destroyed homes and other structures to the sum of 300 million dollars. A peak year for tornadoes was 1967, when 912 "twisters" were spawned in the United States, killing 116 people.

In an effort to reduce as much as possible the toll taken by tornadoes, the National Weather Service maintains a warning system similar to that employed for hurricanes. Headquarters for the tornado watchers is at the National Severe Storm Forecast Center, Kansas City, Missouri. Here meteorologists pore over countless pieces of data relating to the atmospheric conditions over the 48

The destructive power of tornado winds is vividly shown by this scene of complete devastation. The skeleton of a large truck leans against a tree that has been reduced almost to a stump.

adjacent states. They search for those telltale items in the ever changing pattern of the weather that can lead to tornadoes. These experts concentrate their searchings where low pressure centers develop, areas of upset atmospheric conditions caused by the meeting of cool and warm air masses.

The data these experts work with floods into the Center from all over the nation. This information is gathered from hundreds of local weather-observing stations with the help of conventional and long-used weather instruments. The data is also in the form of summaries prepared from radar findings and from photographs of the earth's cloud cover taken by orbiting weather satellites. Other sources of data include instrument-carrying balloons and commercial airline pilots crisscrossing the nation at high altitudes.

Computers are an indispensable tool used by the weather experts at the tornado Forecast Center to help them sift the mass of information. Theirs is a continuous task that goes on without letup twenty-four hours a day, seven days a week.

The tornado seekers at the Forecast Center cannot pinpoint precisely where or predict when twisters will form and strike. But through their studies they can determine where in a general area thunderstorms are most likely to come into existence and possibly unleash highly destructive tornadoes. These predictions have proven remarkably accurate within areas approximately 140 miles wide and 240 miles long. When such zones of possible danger have

This is a view of a tornado on a weather station's radarscope.

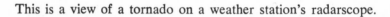

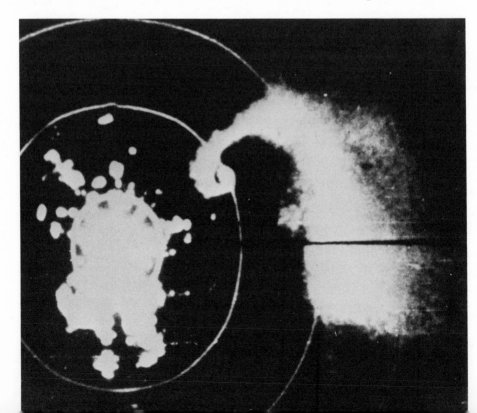

been located on a weather map, the Forecast Center issues the first of two types of warnings to the public, the tornado watch.

The tornado watch bulletin designates the area covered by the alert and sets a period of time when the possibility of tornadoes' coming into existence is particularly great. The watch is teletyped to local National Weather Service offices. The latter in turn relay the cautionary alert to the public with the help of radio and television broadcasts and newspapers in and around the threatened zone. Police, emergency groups, storm spotters and others are also alerted by the tornado watch.

When the tornado watch is announced, weathermen try to make it absolutely clear that this does not mean a tornado is about to strike. It is merely a precaution to inform the public that these devastating storms may appear. People are advised to continue their normal activities but to keep in mind this possibility of storm danger. In the event that an actual tornado is sighted, either through a volunteer observer or radar, the local National Weather Service office immediately announces the threat with a tornado alert, the second of its storm emergency announcements.

The tornado alert sent out tells the location of the twister at the time of detection, the area through which it is expected to travel, and the length of time the tornado will be moving through a threatened area. When the tornado alert is issued, using all channels of modern communications, people in the path of the storm are urgently advised to take swift safety measures.

Emergency groups have compiled a series of safety rules that people in tornado-threatened localities should try to keep in mind for their own protection and self-preservation. These rules include the advice that if a person should be walking the streets at the time of the tornado alert announcement, the individual should go immediately into the nearest building, preferably one of steel and concrete. Once inside, a person should stay as far away from windows as possible.

People living in frame houses, which are highly vulnerable to the

Dashing for the nearest strong shelter when a tornado is about to strike.

tornado's destructive power, should go quickly to the basement. Here, if available, they should crawl under a strongly built workbench or a heavy table. In homes without basements, protection should be taken under heavy furniture in the central part of the house. For all houses in the path of the "twister," windows should be left partially open. This will help to minimize the explosive effect caused by the tornado's partial vacuum. Small rooms, such as bathrooms or closets, afford good protection since they are among the strongest structural areas in a house.

The emergency groups also advise that where schools are threatened by tornadoes, students should gather along the interior hallways on the lowest floor of the school. Auditoriums and gymnasiums should be avoided by all means. If a school is not of steel and concrete construction, students should be marched to the nearest such structure, if there is one. Otherwise they should be led into the open and made to lie flat in a ravine or ditch. This is also suggested for anyone who happens to be caught in the open country in the path of a tornado.

Motorists who may be caught in the open with a "twister" bearing down upon them are urged to drive off the highway at right angles to the storm with all possible speed. This should be done whether a side road exists or not. The main objective is to get out of the way of the tornado.

In many rural areas where tornadoes are more or less common, people have built storm cellars for protection. These underground shelters are usually made of sturdy logs or timbers, concrete blocks or bricks, covered with a heavy layer of solidly packed soil. A strong door leads into the shelter which also has a ventilation pipe sticking through the top. The storm cellars, also popularly called

When a tornado warning is sounded, people caught on the highway stop their cars and head for the nearest ditch.

"scare holes," are built some distance from the main house. This is done to prevent the cellar from being smothered by debris in the event the house is torn to splinters by the "twister." Many a family in the American Midwest have thanked their lucky stars for these underground havens of safety while a killer tornado roared by overhead.

CHAPTER SIX

Thunderstorm

The thunderstorm is the most common and familiar of all the violent weather disturbances. Meteorologists tell us that at any given moment of the day about 1800 thunderstorms are crackling and booming somewhere over the earth's surface. Common though they may be, thunderstorms are not the harmless weather events we tend to consider them. The more severe of these storms can bring much grief to an area, with death and injuries to hundreds of people and extensive property damage.

Severe thunderstorms can be truly spectacular with huge, billowing cumulus clouds piling one upon another in soaring, massive towers to the vaultless sky. The topmost portions of the immense storm-cloud structure may be touched with a rosy glow, reflecting the rays of a hidden sun. But most of the cloud mass, especially the lower region, is in dark, angry shadow. This is the frightening face of the storm. As the ever changing menacing cloud mass moves steadily closer to an observer, it is accompanied by lightning flashes and the roll of thunder. Thus we are impressed by the storm's might not only through our eyes but also through our ears.

There is an uneasy, uncomfortable stillness in the air just minutes before a thunderstorm breaks. It is warm and humid. Soon the fringe of the storm is overhead and we feel its arrival with a blast of cool air and the first spattering of raindrops. Then the thunderstorm strikes with all its fury, unleashing torrents of rain, sometimes mixed with hailstones, and violent, powerful gusts of wind. At this moment too the lightning flashes are almost blinding in their fre-

Cumulonimbus clouds often precede the buildup of a thunderstorm.

quency and the thunder booms with earsplitting salvos. But the thunderstorm is not one of nature's longest moods of anger and soon the noise, the rain, and the wind fade quietly off into the distance. Though a thunderstorm's visit may have been an unpleasant one in some respects, it always brings some good too. The air is generally left cooler and more refreshing while a parched earth may have been given much-needed moisture.

How do thunderstorms form? As we have mentioned from time to time in the earlier pages, these storms come about because of unsettled atmospheric conditions. And one of the more common ways that the atmosphere becomes unsettled is the result of clashes between cool and warm air masses. One of the early signs in the beginning of a thunderstorm is the formation of cumulus and

114

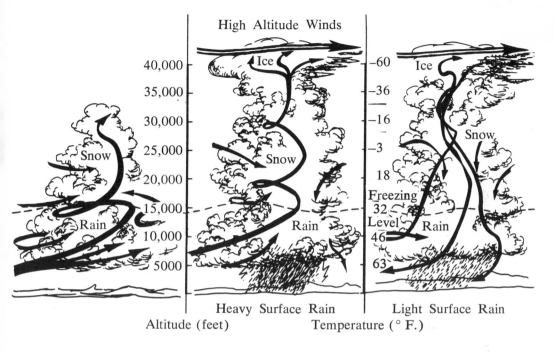

High Altitude Winds

Altitude (feet)	Temperature (° F.)

Heavy Surface Rain   Light Surface Rain

THREE STAGES OF A THUNDERSTORM

Adapted from *Thunderstorms*—ESSA, National Oceanic and Atmospheric Administration

BEGINNING

Acting on converging surface winds, a strong updraft carries warm, moist air past condensation levels. Cumulus clouds form. Vertical growth of storm clouds is helped by air entering from sides of cloud formation; heat energy is released by condensing water vapor and outflowing air at top of storm clouds.

MAXIMUM

Rain and snow begin to fall within storm clouds. Ice particles form in the towering, anvil-shaped topmost clouds of the storm. The thunderstorm is at its maximum stage with formation and falling of hail or rain. Downdrafts of cool air now join the updrafts and lightning begins.

ENDING

Downdrafts of cool air eventually break up the storm formation. Surface winds no longer converge but flow in many different directions. Updrafts lose their source of energy. Clouds separate and scatter. Precipitation weakens and then stops. Downdrafts of air also end. The storm is no longer a unified powerhouse of energy.

cumulonimbus clouds. These are the massive, bulging cloud forms that move so majestically across the sky. The clouds are born by the process of convection, which involves the vertical rising of warm, moist air to higher and cooler altitudes. Here the water vapor of the air is cooled and condensed into minute water droplets. Clouds are the visible result of this condensation.

A number of factors can be responsible for launching the warm, moist air on its upward journey. Two opposing and contrasting surface air currents, a warm and a cool, can converge at some point in a frontal zone. The two converging air currents generally meet in the center of a low pressure area. The cool air, being

Clouds such as these often accompany the high winds that occur in the lee of the Front Range of the Colorado Rockies in the winter and spring. These clouds were photographed near Boulder, Colorado.

heavier and perhaps stronger in movement, may wedge itself beneath the lighter, warm air, starting the latter on its upward movement. Once begun, this updraft of warm air can be vigorous and continuous up to high altitudes where the condensation takes place.

A warm, moist air mass may also be started on a vertical moving path when it encounters a mountain slope. Bouncing from this immovable barrier, the air current is deflected upward.

The cumulus clouds are the advance guard of the vertical soaring warm air mass. These clouds do not remain static but are in a constant state of vigorous activity and change, mainly because of the continuing process of convection. Now the visible part of the continuously rising warm air mass, they grow steadily into the familiar tier upon tier, domelike cumulonimbus clouds so familiar during thunderstorms.

One may wonder what force keeps the warm air mass rising once this movement is started. There are several. The first may be another source of air flowing into the cloud from the sides, mixing with and feeding the updraft. Weather experts call this process "entrainment." Another force is the chimney effect. This gets its name from the fact that air can rush through a vertically rising hollow structure with considerable speed. In cumulonimbus cloud formations there are numerous such hollow areas through which the air can speedily move.

A third force, and perhaps one of the most important in maintaining and strengthening an upward-rising air current, is heat energy. This is produced when the water vapor of the warm air mass is changed into tiny water droplets. The speed of the process by which this heat energy is produced, or released, is directly related to the amount of gaseous water vapor converted into liquid water.

And so the monstrous thunderheads continue to grow, billowing ever higher and becoming darker and more menacing. The storm's topmost clouds can reach into the stratosphere, often to altitudes of more than eight miles. At peak heights strong horizontal winds

Photo shows the top of thunderclouds as seen by the camera's eye aboard the Apollo 9 spaceship. The storm was over the Amazon Basin, Brazil, at the time the picture was taken.

tear at the cumulus clouds, flattening and shaping their top portions into the form of an anvil. The anvil shape is a distinct feature of high-soaring cumulonimbus thunderheads and usually can be seen many miles distant from the storm.

During the cloud formation and soaring activity, other events are simultaneously taking place within the thunderstorm's power-generating interior, such as the production of rain. After water droplets are formed from the condensation of the rising warm air's water vapor, they are buffeted about by the vigorously upward-moving air current. In the course of this agitation the water droplets bump into one another and frequently stick together to become big water drops. When these reach such a size and weight that the rising vertical air current can no longer support them, they fall to earth as rain.

118

It often happens that the upward-rising air currents within thunderstorms are so strong that they will carry water droplets to extremely high altitudes. When this occurs, the water droplets will freeze into lumps of ice, the familiar hailstones which often clatter down from thunderstorms. Just as with the smaller water droplets at lower altitudes, the hailstones are bounced about and often stick together to become bigger and heavier ice particles. When this happens, the updraft of air is no longer strong enough to keep the hailstones aloft. Heavyweights now—some hailstones can become as big as golf balls—they fall through the clouds with considerable speed to the earth's surface.

It is at the point when rain or hailstones are falling that the

Characteristic of many thunderstorms is the anvil cloud formation shaped by swift winds at altitudes of more than 30,000 feet.

thunderstorm reaches its full power and growth. Further evidence of the storm's mature stage is the presence of lightning. These electrical flashes commence with the start of precipitation.

At one time it was thought that the processes just described took place within a single huge thunderstorm formation. Now the accepted idea is that the thunderstorm cloud formation is made up of many separate units, or cells as the weather expert calls them, wherein the air-current activity, rain formation, and all the other storm processes can be starting, reaching their maximum stage, or fading away. The visible signs of this cell activity may be seen in the constantly changing shapes of the towering, bulging thunderhead clouds.

Falling rain or hailstones begin another stage in the life history of a thunderstorm. In the course of falling to earth, they trigger a downward flow of air. This is the cool air one feels from a thunderstorm shortly after the first raindrops spatter on the earth's surface.

Just as the updraft has its sources of energy, so does the downdraft. The flow of the latter, started by falling rain or hail, is strengthened by air moving through the sides of a cloud and by a cooling effect through evaporation. This latter process comes about through a complicated interaction between the air flowing through the sides of a cloud and falling precipitation. The cooler the down-

This schematic drawing shows the structure and movement of a thunderstorm.

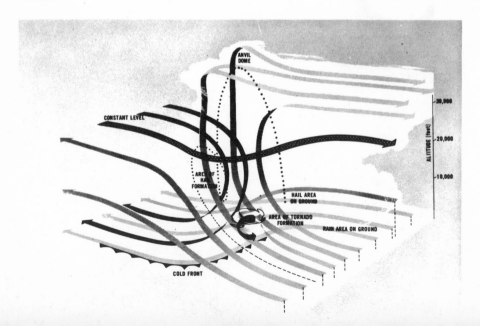

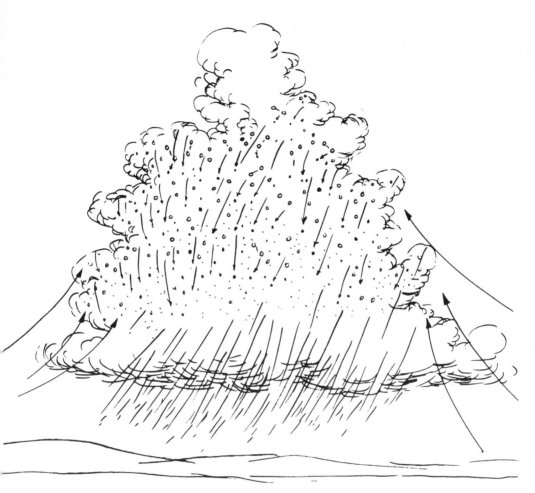

Rain formation in cumulonimbus cloud

draft becomes, the heavier the air becomes, which helps to speed its downward movement.

Lightning and thunder are the highlights of any thunderstorm. Both have awed and struck fear into man since his earliest presence on earth. Because of their mysterious, frightening aspects, lightning and thunder were made a part of the religion of many ancient and primitive societies. Places seared by a lightning stroke were sometimes made sacred thereafter.

The surging sudden power of a lightning stroke is the most destructive aspect of a thunderstorm.

Lightning is the spectacular, secondary effect of a thunderstorm's electrification. Just how this electrification comes about is a question that continues to stump weather experts. All are agreed that the processes involved with its creation, and hence that of lightning, are enormously complex.

In the eighteenth century there was a strong suspicion among scientists that lightning and electricity were one and the same. It was Benjamin Franklin, a man with an enormous curiosity in scientific matters, who proved the relationship with his famous kite experiment.

By flying a kite during a local thunderstorm, Franklin attracted

122

an electrical charge down the kite string following a lightning flash. The charge caused the frayed ends of parts of the string to stand out rigidly. Faint sparks also appeared at the string ends. When Franklin saw this he passed his knuckles close to a metal key which he had tied to the kite string. Stronger sparks crackled between his knuckles and the key.

After analyzing the happenings of his experiment Franklin concluded that lightning and electricity were the same. The fact that he was able to report on the results of this experiment was nothing short of a miracle. The lightning flash could have electrocuted Franklin on the spot.

Since Franklin's day, weather scientists have found out a good deal more about the enormous electrical force that builds up within a thunderstorm and its lightning offspring. As storm clouds grow in size, so too does an electrical charge within the bounds of the storm area. Inside the storm cloud system this electrical charge is predominantly made up of positive electrical particles. These are concentrated in the cold topmost portions of the clouds. In the lower half of the clouds is a large zone of negative particles surrounding a much smaller area that is positive in nature.

While all this electrical activity is going on within the storm clouds, similar electrical stirrings are taking place in the earth directly below the storm mass. The electrical force that is normally within the earth is mainly of a negative character. But in that part of the earth over which the storm is moving, and for several miles beyond its perimeter, a transformation takes place. The earth-bound negative charges are turned into positive charges. The change-over is due primarily to the influence of the negative force in the base of the storm clouds moving above.

The ground charge, now positive, keeps moving at about the same rate as the storm system. All the while it is increasing in force, just as the negative cloud charge is also growing in strength. As the two opposing charges become intensified, they are strongly attracted toward each other. This strong desire to meet causes the ground positive charges to travel up tall buildings, trees, or other high objects in an effort to reach the negative cloud field. At first this joining together is prevented by the air mass that exists between cloud and ground. The air acts as a kind of insulating barrier. The separation continues until the electrical charges in the cloud and ground grow so powerful that they overcome the air barrier.

The electrical potential—the difference between the negative and positive charges, which creates the conducting or electrical roadway along which the current between the two opposing forces flows—can be as high as 100 million volts. This represents enor-

Electrical relationship between a storm cloud and the earth leading to the formation of a lightning stroke

mous power and makes the lightning stroke a highly destructive force. Lightning flashes traveling along this conductive path almost always go from negative (cloud) to positive (ground) charges. However, these extremely powerful electrical strokes can also dart from cloud to cloud and from ground to cloud where high objects serve as a springboard.

Research in the field of lightning has unveiled the mechanics of this phenomenon of thunderstorms and shown them to be rather complex. The typical cloud-to-ground stroke begins with what the meteorologist calls a "pilot leader." This is the first, faint flash of electricity, so weak that it cannot be seen by the naked eye. Directed earthward, the pilot leader starts the conductive path along which the lightning flash will eventually travel.

Another and stronger surge of current, identified as the "step leader," follows in the wake of the pilot. This second electrical surge performs like the flashing tongue of a cobra as it darts toward earth some 100 feet or more at a flash. The step leader strikes downward again and again, pushing the conductive path of electrified or ionized particles ever closer to the ground.

While the pilot and step leaders have been blazing a path for the subsequent full lightning stroke, the ground charge has not been idle. Its electrical charge has been building up in strength along with the cloud charge. When this has reached a particular point, the ground charge sends electrified streamers upward probing the atmosphere in an effort to connect with the electrical current flashing down from the clouds. As the connection is made, the electrified channel between ground and cloud is completed.

Once the electrified path is completed, a return lightning stroke streaks upward with the speed of light (186,282 miles per second). This flash illuminates the downward-moving leader tracks. Because these tracks are pointing earthward we get the impression that the lightning stroke is darting from the clouds. Actually, much of this electrical force is from the ground charge.

The dazzling light of the return stroke is made by atoms and

125

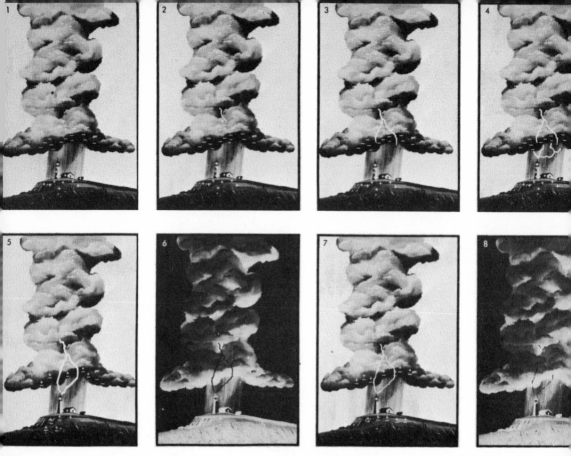

LIFE CYCLE OF A LIGHTNING STROKE

As thunderstorm induces growing positive charge in earth, potential between cloud and ground increases (1) until pilot leader starts a conductive channel toward ground (2) followed by step leaders (3) which move downward for short intervals (4) until met by streamers from ground. Return stroke from ground illuminates branches (5) and seems to come from cloud. Main stroke is followed by sequence of dart leaders and returns (6, 7) until potential is reduced or ionized path is dispersed (8). Elapsed time: about one second.

Chart and Key adapted from *Guide*—World Meteorological Organization

molecules in the air that have been energized by the lightning flash. The cloud-to-ground lightning stroke is the more familiar one we see from a thunderstorm.

Step leaders are also involved in the movement of lightning from ground to cloud. These advance flashes usually make their departure for the clouds from a variety of tall objects—buildings and trees are among the more common—that serve as good conductors of electricity. The major difference between lightning strokes that

126

leap upward from the ground and those darting earthward from the clouds is the absence of a return flash from the former. Meteorologists believe the reason for this is the poor mobility of cloud-based electrical charges as compared to those in the earth.

This description of lightning strokes may seem complex and lengthy. But there is nothing lengthy about the passage of a lightning flash, which is completed in just about one second.

Lightning flashes are always accompanied by the crash and boom of thunder, the sound effect that has given the thunderstorm its name. Thunder is the result of a swift expansion and heating of the air through which a lightning stroke passes. The air expands with explosive rapidity.

Thunder occurs in different forms. When a lightning stroke is near at hand, the thunder that follows almost immediately is an earsplitting explosive boom. Lightning strokes that take place some distance away produce thunder sounds that are more familiarly associated with this storm—a rolling, rumbling noise. This distinctive thunder sound is caused mainly by the upset atmospheric conditions in the area of the thunderstorm.

Anyone who likes to indulge in mathematics and at the same time feel like an amateur meteorologist can easily determine the distance between himself and a far-off lightning stroke. This is done by counting the number of seconds between the flash of lightning and the crash of thunder. The resulting figure is then divided by five, which gives an approximate distance in miles.

Lightning, like thunder, exists in a number of different types. The lightning stroke from cloud-to-ground is the most common. It can charge from black, angry storm clouds as a single streak or several streaks. When striking in the latter manner, lightning is usually of the forked variety, which vividly lights up the conducting channels of the stroke.

Sometimes we see lightning as a flashing glow, lighting up a darkened sky at intervals. This is called sheet lightning. It usually covers a broad expanse of the sky and, for the most part, travels from cloud to cloud.

A variation of sheet lightning is a type known as heat lightning. This is often seen in summer on a hot, humid night, flashing along the horizon. Meteorologists believe that heat lightning is the reflection of lightning strokes from a thunderstorm far beyond the horizon.

Still another variety of lightning is the ribbon type. This form is brought into existence by the action of high winds, but it actually is a variation of the more common streak lightning. Ribbon lightning travels in what appears to be successive, parallel paths.

Beaded lightning is another type of lightning whose single, continuous flash is broken into a series of separate sections. Powerful, erratic wind currents may be responsible for breaking the stroke into short flashes and hence giving it the name beaded.

Perhaps the most interesting of all lightning strokes is ball lightning. Just as its name indicates, this is actually a glowing, ball-shaped form of lightning that streaks from thunderclouds like a cannon shot. In addition to its round form this type of lightning may also take a doughnut shape and even that of an ellipsoid.

Ball lightning can be terribly alarming, striking with a hissing sound. It also may travel crazily, and with tremendous swiftness, rolling along wherever it happens to have landed. Sometimes this unique type of lightning may not even come to earth but will hang suspended in the air momentarily. Weather scientists who are lightning specialists find ball lightning an excellent subject on which to start a heated discussion. The reason for this is that there are so many different ideas as to both the origin of ball lightning and the shapes it assumes.

One of the newest scientific theories concerning ball lightning is that it may be a mixture of extremely hot air and soot or similar material brought together after a lightning stroke hits a tree or other object.

Torrential wind-driven rain, crackling lightning flashes, and the crash of thunder mark the peak development and power of the thunderstorm. This great powerhouse of energy may send its surg-

Ball lightning has been described as floating, short-lived globes of light that spring from thunderstorm clouds. This old woodcut shows a trio of farm workers startled by this rare form of lightning.

ing, dome-shaped clouds to heights of more than eight miles. At the bottom, the clouds may spread over an area of several square miles. The fury and noise of the tempest, however, are not long-lived. The thunderstorm generally blows over a particular area in less than an hour.

We on the ground directly beneath a thunderstorm are first made aware of the storm's maturity by the beginning downpour of rain and cool blast of wind. Interestingly enough, the cool draft of air that sweeps toward the earth from the upper reaches of the thunderclouds is also a signal that the storm's ending stage is about to start. Weathermen have learned through their studies of count-less thunderstorms that the first cool downdraft of air may occur even without rain and by itself signal that the storm is at its height.

As the thunderstorm rages, the cool downdraft of air becomes increasingly more powerful and eventually overcomes the flow of warm air sweeping upward. What happens is that the converging winds at the earth's surface, which initially played a big role in getting the storm started and then feeding its development, are now blocked off from flowing into the storm. Without the upsweep-ing warm, moist winds to fuel the thunderstorm, it dies a swift death. Rain stops, cool, gusty winds die, and the thunderclouds are torn apart by swift winds at high altitudes and blown away.

It is probably because of their frequency that thunderstorms are

Man is almost helpless in his efforts to control a lightning-caused forest fire. This one destroyed a huge area of Bitterroot National Forest, Montana.

A forest devastated by a fire that was started by lightning.

not generally thought of as being dangerous. In reality, they are major destroyers of life and property. Lightning, rain, wind, and hail, powerful elements of the thunderstorm, can bring great destruction to man and his surroundings.

Lightning is probably the greatest of the thunderstorm's destructive forces. In the United States lightning kills about 150 people a year. Almost ten times this many people suffer injuries caused by lightning.

Property damage that lightning achieves, mainly by fire, is also enormous. Thousands of acres of valuable timberland are destroyed annually in the United States through lightning-caused fires. The United States Forest Service, which is concerned with the care of the nation's timber resources, has found that in the twenty-year period 1942–1962 this country had more than 140,000 lightning-caused fires. The destruction to timber, wildlife, vegetation, and watersheds is almost beyond estimating.

Of course lightning does not select only forests for doing its destructive work. Man-built structures—homes and farm buildings, among others—power facilities, and aircraft are also frequent victims of the lightning bolt. Property damage in the United States due to lightning is estimated to be more than one hundred million dollars annually.

Floods caused by torrential rains from thunderclouds can destroy almost on the same scale as lightning. These are most dangerous as flash floods, where a dry creek bed or other low-lying terrain suddenly becomes inundated by powerful, heaving currents of water. Roaring along at full strength, such floods can carry away just about anything in their path.

The winds of a thunderstorm are no mean destroyers too. Gusting with great force, thunderstorm winds can do enormous damage by blowing down trees, utility poles, radio and television antennas, signs and rooftops. Plate-glass windows are also frequent victims, either shattered under wind pressure or broken by flying missiles. Even parts of brick and stone buildings have been ripped loose and thrown to the ground.

Hailstones from a thunderstorm are probably the least damaging of this tempest's features. However, if they are big enough and fall over a period of time with intensity, hailstones can do considerable destruction. For example, a farm crop that took weeks to grow can be battered to a total loss within a few brief minutes.

Many people have the erroneous impression that thunderstorms are harmless in nature, but these weather disturbances should not be taken lightly. As we have seen, this holds true especially for those areas where tornadoes spring from thunderstorms. We have already mentioned the safety precautions the National Weather Service urges people to take concerning these. But it also has safety advice regarding the thunderstorm's other characteristics, lightning in particular.

Portions of Colorado are frequent victims of damaging hailstorms. The corn in this field in northeast Colorado was battered and broken by severe hail that fell from a summer thunderstorm.

There is no certain way that one can escape being struck by lightning. The danger can be minimized, however, by following a few simple rules. When a storm is about to strike, seek shelter indoors. If you are in the open you may be the highest object for some distance around you. In that case you will serve as an excellent lightning conductor and thus become a victim of this electrical force. Should you be caught outdoors when a thunderstorm breaks, avoid standing beneath trees, which are favorite targets of lightning strokes.

When indoors during a thunderstorm, do not handle electrical

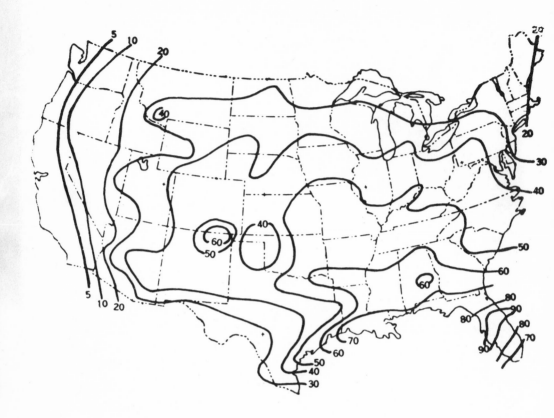

This map chart shows the average number of thunderstorms throughout the United States in the course of a year.

appliances. Keep the television set turned off; stay away from windows.

In rural areas creek beds should be avoided during a thunderstorm because of the danger of flash floods. Anyone living along a riverbank should remain alert to the danger of rain-swollen waters.

Thunderstorms are the most common expression of nature's angry moods. They are vivid, noisy spectacles of the sky that weather experts find one of the more interesting areas of study in their complex field of meteorology.

134

CHAPTER SEVEN

Winter
Storms

So far we have talked about storms that for the most part take place in the temperate zone during the summer season of the year. What of the colder months, the wintertime? This too can be a period of weather disturbances, bringing bone-cracking cold, sleet, and paralyzing blizzards to our earthly way of life.

Winter storms are not very different from some of the summer storms, both in their structure and in the way they are generated. Most winter tempests are cyclonic in nature, with extensive swirling clouds moving in a counterclockwise direction. They spring from the same weather conditions, the perennial struggles between cold polar air masses and warm tropical air movements. Since the

A hailstorm is a frequent visitor, winter or summer.

northern half of the earth is colder in winter, the sun having traveled far below the equator, the churning weather front is usually dominated by frigid air masses that unleash stinging forces of cold, ice, and snow.

The spinning clouds of the winter storm do not as a rule form a vortex, which is such a common feature of hurricanes and tornadoes. But the cloud mass ranges over a vast area, often thousands of square miles. On the weather map these wintry storms are indicated as intense low pressure systems.

There are numerous places in the north temperate zone where these intense low pressure systems frequently get their start. One of the farthest of these spawning grounds is in the extreme western Pacific off the coast of Asia. The trouble spot begins where the polar front and a warm air mass clash over the ocean. A fully developed storm from this area catches a strong eastward-moving

An enlarged view of a section of a hailstone.

This giant hailstone, which fell at Coffeyville, Kansas, is probably the largest ever recorded in the United States. It weighed 1.6 pounds and measured 17½ inches in circumference.

wind current and eventually dumps much of its winter cargo on Alaska.

There is another source for winter storms in the Pacific that lies roughly over the north-central part of that ocean. This too exists along a front where frigid Arctic air and warm air from farther south wage a contest for supremacy. The resulting storm also rides an eastward-moving wind system but along a more southerly course, and strikes the western coasts of Canada and the United States. Sometimes far-ranging outriders of such a winter disturbance, bearing cold wind and rain, penetrate deep into normally mild southern California, bringing extreme discomfort to the people there.

In most cases the winter storms born in the two areas just men-

Special snow-blowing machines are used to clear airport runways of snow. The activities at airports can be quickly halted by a snowstorm.

tioned die out over the western sections of the American continent. The Rocky Mountains stand as a barrier that forces the storm to break up against its high slopes. From time to time a Pacific tempest will be strong enough to hurdle the Rockies. However, by the time it reaches the eastern side of the mountains much of its power has been destroyed. But again, there are exceptions. In some instances a storm that has managed to get over the Rocky Mountains will regroup its forces, intensify, and continue its eastward movement. When this happens the mid-portion of the United States usually catches the full force of the storm's power—cold winds, snow, or even blizzard conditions. One of the favorite areas where these Pacific storms like to recover their power lies just to the east of the Colorado Rockies. Because of this, weathermen call such storms Colorado cyclones.

138

There are occasions when the eastward-traveling Pacific storms will take a more northerly route and, instead of dying out completely along Canada's Pacific coast, will make their way over the Canadian Rockies. East of these mountains the storm will build up to a new intensity before continuing its journey to the middle region of the American continent. Storms that follow this path are identified as Alberta cyclones.

Very often both the Colorado and Alberta cyclones will regain new power at about the same time and take off for the interior of the continent. Eventually the two will bump into each other over the Great Lakes and combine their wintry fury. The doubly intense storm becomes a major disturbance and the regions bordering the Lakes are usually swept by biting cold winds and buried under mountains of snow. The Great Lakes region is along the storm track for many winter cyclones.

The eastern seaboard of the United States sometimes catches the full blast of the wind, cold, and snow of a winter storm traveling from the Great Lakes. More often, however, this part of the United States is visited by winter tempests that are spawned right in its own back yard, off the coast of Virginia and the Carolinas or farther west in a broad region between the coast and the Appalachian Mountains.

As the swirling pattern of these storms begins and develops, they generally move in a northerly direction up along the Atlantic coast. There is nothing anemic about these tempests. They can bring paralyzing snowfalls and bitterly cold winds.

Because of the counterclockwise motion of the cloud structure of these storms, they appear to be coming from the northeast. As an actual fact, this is true only for the swirling winds and clouds. The basic movement or main thrust of the body of the storm is in a northward direction. But due to the directional force of the storm's winds and clouds, this tempest is often referred to as a "nor'easter."

Northeasters also occur in spring and fall, but not very often during the summer months. They bring torrential rains and strong winds. The disturbance may last several days. At the peak of intensity, wind speeds of a northeaster may not be far removed from those of a hurricane. Indeed, areas that are severely battered by a storm of this kind very often mistake it for a hurricane. However, the clouds, temperature and rain patterns are completely different.

The winter storms of the Atlantic seaboard usually take themselves out over the ocean and move off to Europe in the direction of Iceland. By the time they reach this area the storm's characteristics have all but disappeared. Not all storms move into the Icelandic low and die out, however. Severe winter storms occasionally move into Europe from the Atlantic.

Winter storms can bring numerous discomforts to the areas they visit. Snow, sleet, and numbing cold winds are the best known of these. Surpassing all, of course, by its frequency and severity is snow.

By itself, a single snowflake is one of the most exquisite creations of nature. Accumulated falls of snow, however, can be a disaster, especially to cities. Snow, like a cloud, forms in the atmosphere by condensation of water vapor in temperatures that are below freezing. As is the case in the creation of a raindrop, the snowflake takes form around some minute particle in the air, usually a speck of dust. This symbol of winter when fully developed is made up of a number of opaque ice crystals. The whiteness of the snowflake is due to the reflective nature of the tiny crystals of which it consists. Light rebounds from the countless surfaces of the crystals rather than being absorbed.

Snow crystals most commonly assume beautiful, lacy hexagonal patterns. Amazingly, no two are ever alike. Sometimes they are star-shaped or formed like a pin with a hexagonal head. Big fluffy snowflakes may also attach themselves to one another, making cone-shaped objects that float to earth point first. Snowflakes joined with others can reach a size three and four inches in diameter.

The condition of the winter atmosphere pretty much deter-

140

mines what the snowflake will be like by the time it strikes the earth. It may start out from the cloud in which it was formed as an average-sized snowflake, then change to rain as it nears the earth if the temperature is above freezing.

Snow may also fall in two other forms, snow grains and snow pellets. Snow grains are minute, opaque particles of ice. Their fall may be compared to the summertime drizzle. This variety of snow is hard and generally lands without bouncing or shattering when striking solid earth objects.

Snow pellets—also known as soft hail or tapioca snow—are ice particles too, small and opaque. They are softer in physical structure, however, and can be easily crushed between the fingers. When snow pellets hit a hard surface they rebound and frequently will shatter. They usually occur together with ordinary snow or just before it begins to fall.

Weather experts include snow as part of their precipitation measurements. Ten inches of snow have been estimated to be equal to one inch of rainfall. A winter's storm of a cargo of snow can beautify a landscape as well as create some king-sized headaches for man's earth-bound activities. Freshly fallen snow can sculpture trees, buildings, and the earth into a dazzling fairyland of white, enchanting youngsters and oldsters alike. At the same time it may be of such a nature and quantity as to block forms of land transportation, obstruct the movement of people, and destroy property. This last is accomplished by heavy accumulations of snow which, in many instances, is blown into huge drifts by strong, gusting winds. In brief, severe snowstorms can immobilize cities and trap travelers on highways and railroads. A winter storm can make life equally hazardous for rural areas by isolating people from food and fuel supplies and medical attention. For those areas where raising cattle is an important economic activity, snowstorms can be especially disastrous. Under abnormally severe winter conditions herds can be decimated through hunger, thirst, and cold.

Areas that have experienced severe winter snowstorms can also expect a delayed unpleasantness. When spring comes and the snow cover melts, floods often result. For localities near rivers, this can be quite destructive, especially if spring rains add to the floodwaters.

Snowstorms, however, are not all bad. They do bring some good. For example, a heavy snow cover over farmlands serves as a kind of protective blanket preventing strong winter winds from blowing away precious topsoil. Also, when the snow melts it furnishes needed nutrients and water.

Many localities, particularly in mountainous areas, like to see snowstorms for economic reasons. A thick mantle of snow on the mountain slopes provides recreation in the form of winter sports—skiing, tobogganing, sleigh riding, and zipping over hill and dale aboard a snowmobile.

Looking at snowstorms from a world view, they are builders of glaciers in many parts of the earth, thereby contributing vitally to man's essential water supply.

Cleaning up at busy Newark Airport after a heavy snowfall.

Snow can bring economic benefits to some areas that offer skiing and other winter sports activities.

Snowstorms occur in varying intensities. The worst and most spectacular is the blizzard. Features that distinguish this winter storm are cold, strong winds and blinding snow. Weather experts have placed this storm in two categories. The first is of blizzards that have winds of at least 35 miles per hour, temperatures of 20 degrees F. or lower, and heavy falling or windblown snow. The snowfall is of such intensity that visibility is reduced to less than 500 feet. These storm conditions usually last for a considerable period of time.

The second type of blizzard, the severest, has winds that may howl at a speed of better than 45 miles per hour and that are accompanied by temperatures of 10 degrees F. or lower. Falling or wind-blown snow may be so thick and blinding that visibility is cut to almost zero. There is nothing soft or mushy about snow that falls in any kind of a blizzard. It is fine, dry, and powdery and when driven by the wind can sting one's face in a most uncomfortable manner.

Snowstorms of the blizzard variety occur most frequently in the United States in the northern plains states and as far south as Texas. Blizzards are also no strangers to the central states, the New England states, and New York.

There have been some monumental blizzards in the long history of weather record keeping. One of the worst occurred over a period from January 11 to 13 in 1888. Almost the entire midwest portion of the United States from the Rockies eastward and from the Canadian border south to Texas was blasted by polar winds, buried under mountains of snow, and numbed by deadly cold. Scores of people lost their lives, cattle by the hundreds died, and property loss was enormous.

During that same year a memorable blizzard that raged from March 11 to March 14 struck large sections of the mid-Atlantic and New England states. The storm came as a complete surprise because by that time of the year spring was almost at hand. Thereafter, the blizzard of '88, as the storm popularly came to be called,

144

Part of the devastation in the downtown area of New York City caused by the great blizzard that struck in March of 1888.

was a favorite topic of conversation whenever winter storms were discussed.

This Atlantic winter storm paralyzed a coastal region extending from Chesapeake Bay to Maine. The average snowfall was 40 inches. Mountainous drifts, nearly 6 feet high, were formed by fierce, cold winds. New York City was one of the more seriously hit localities. All activity within this metropolitan center was brought to a complete standstill. Clearing the streets of huge mounds of snow so people could move around for obtaining needed food and fuel supplies proved especially difficult. When the toll of the storm was finally counted, some 200 inhabitants of New York City had died while more than twice that number had succumbed for the entire storm-stricken area.

Perhaps as a reminder from nature that the killing storms of yesteryear are not a thing of the past, a winter tempest of about the same major proportions as the blizzard of '88 came again to the United States in 1966. From January 29 to 31 of that year a blizzard that was catastrophic in its severity paralyzed the Atlantic coast region from Virginia to New England. Cold, an avalanche of snow, and bitter winds brought all types of human outdoor activity to a complete halt. Of the more than fifty people who lost their lives in this polar onslaught, a number were among thousands trapped in stranded automobiles.

Not too long thereafter, another blizzard hit the midwestern United States on the second of March through the fifth, burying areas under 3 feet of snow. In some places the snow was piled in drifts 30 feet high, blown by winds that reached 100 miles per hour in gusts. By the time this winter tempest disappeared, fifteen persons had died.

The winter storms talked about up to this point have been of the type in which falling snow plays a key role. There is another kind, equally deadly and destructive—the ice storm. This occurs when rain or drizzle falls from a comparatively warm upper region of the atmosphere to colder temperatures at the earth's surface. In almost all cases this means temperatures below 32 degrees Fahrenheit. The precipitation starts out in liquid form. Then, upon landing on the colder earth, it freezes and forms a coating of ice on everything it touches.

The coating of ice this kind of storm can put on surface objects may range in thickness from a thin glaze to icy armor an inch thick, although there have been instances of such coatings as thick as an extraordinary 8 inches. This kind of ice deposit is generally highly destructive.

Trees are a common victim of winter ice storms. The weight of

New York City was paralyzed for several days after the blizzard of March 12, 1888. This photo of a snow-clogged street shows the reason why. Note the maze of overhead telephone and electric power lines, common for that era.

147

A winter sleet storm can create a silvery wonderland, and can also cause extensive damage to telephone and power lines.

the ice that may accumulate on their branches can bend them to the breaking point. In one interesting case it was found that an evergreen tree 50 feet high and 20 feet wide could carry a load of as much as 5 tons of ice from a severe ice storm.

Equally vulnerable to the cracking weight of ice are electric power and telephone lines and the poles that carry them. The soft, mushy ice builds itself up layer by layer around wires. Eventually the ice can become so heavy that the utility wires and poles are dragged to the ground. This kind of destruction can play havoc with a modern community that relies so much for its heating, cooking, and lighting on electricity.

Ice storms are probably the worst winter hazards for pedestrians and for motorists on highways. Roads slick with ice are one of the chief causes of winter auto accidents and death. Insurance company statistics show that more than 85 percent of the deaths during severe ice storms are due to ice-coated highways. Pedestrians have an equally difficult time on ice-glazed sidewalks that cause countless falls, often resulting in sprains or broken bones.

In the United States the region most commonly visited by winter ice storms is roughly a wide band from Nebraska, Kansas, and Oklahoma eastward through the middle Atlantic and New England states.

Probably some of the worst ice storms recorded in the history of the National Weather Service have taken place in those states below the Mason-Dixon line. The reason for this is that the Southland generally experiences comparatively mild temperatures through the winter months. Dwellings and field crops as a rule are not protected from winter's icy tentacles. Thus, when an ice storm moves outside its usual northern area to penetrate the deep south, it can cause discomfort and damage on a major scale.

Sometimes ice storms are mistakenly called sleet storms. Sleet is formed when raindrops freeze as hard as tiny pebbles. Unlike the ice of a conventional ice storm, which is soft and mushy when it lands, sleet pellets bounce hither and yon after hitting solid objects. The pellets do not stick to trees or poles like the ice of an ice storm. If sleet pellets continue to fall at such a rate that they begin to accumulate on the ground, they can present a serious danger to both pedestrians and motorists.

The extreme cold and strong winds of winter storms can make that season of the year one of serious discomfort. A quick and severe drop in temperature usually follows a winter storm. The cold is the result of a shift in the wind, which before the storm may have been blowing from the comparatively warm southwest point of the compass. When it switches to the northwest or north, the wind can bring a cold air mass along that will cause the thermometer to drop 15 degrees or more in a matter of a few hours. In the

Midwest and North Central Plains of the United States, this sudden plunge of the thermometer often means a prolonged cold wave with sub-zero temperatures.

If a winter storm has brought a heavy blanket of snow, this too can contribute to the intensity of the cold spell. What happens in this case is that the sun's warming rays are no longer being absorbed by the earth's surface but instead are reflected away into space.

Extreme cold by itself is uncomfortable enough and can cause considerable damage. When it is accompanied by strong winds, it can have the effect of much lower temperatures. It has been estimated that when a strong wind is added to only slightly below freezing cold, the combined effect can be that of a temperature almost fifty degrees lower.

Such extreme winter conditions can chill the body very quickly and lead to such serious consequences as frostbite and lung injury.

Winter can be beautiful and terrible for those regions that experience the changing seasons. The terrible aspect, of course, relates to severe winter storms. As in other periods of the year, the National Weather Service maintains a constant vigil for storms, noting the start of winter tempests, their nature, intensity, path of travel, and other necessary information. Thus warnings of approaching ice storms, heavy snowfalls, blizzards, cold waves, or other disturbances can be quickly passed along to the public.

To be forewarned is to be forearmed, as the saying goes, and so after being given early enough information about an impending winter storm, people who are wise take proper precautionary measures. The National Weather Service has compiled a list of common-sense rules which, if followed, ought to help one get through a storm without serious difficulties.

One should make sure, for example, that battery-powered radio or television equipment is in working order before the storm arrives. Either of these communication devices may be the only vital contact with the outside world beyond a storm-struck area. Also,

150

one should make sure that emergency cooking facilities and flashlights are in good condition.

Winter heating fuel is another essential. Check the storage tank
to see that a proper supply is on hand. If the storm should dump a
heavy blanket of snow on the ground, fuel trucks would find it difficult or impossible to move.

Equally important is to see that there is adequate and even extra
food in stock. The supplies should contain items that require no
cooking or refrigeration because the storm may knock out the electric power.

In trying to keep one's home warm, care must be taken to prevent fire. This is a common disaster that strikes all too many houses

Snow and ice conditions at the mouth of the Lincoln Tunnel in New York
City cause motorists to drive with extreme caution.

and apartments during a storm and in the cold wave that usually follows. Do not overheat coal- or oil-burning stoves, fireplaces, heaters, or furnaces.

An especially important warning is directed to those who cannot wait to get outdoors to shovel away the snow blocking doors, sidewalks, or driveways. Snow shoveling is hard work even for those who are accustomed to physical exertion. Caution is urged because shoveling during and after winter storms is a frequent cause of death through heart attack.

As for people living in rural areas, it is urged that they make all necessary trips for supplies before a storm arrives and not while the tempest is raging. Some kind of emergency heating facility should be prepared, as the chances of a power failure are usually very great. Other emergency items such as camp stoves and oil lamps should be checked to see that they are properly filled and ready to go into needed operation.

It is clear from these few safety instructions that common sense is the governing factor in coping with the hazards of a winter storm. If one indulges in no unnecessary risks, a blizzard or other winter disturbance can be gone through with ease. Indeed, it might even be an exciting, exhilarating experience.

CHAPTER EIGHT

Storm
Control

Will man one day be able to control storms in order to reduce their destructive effects? There is as yet no sure answer to this question, but the promise appears great. We have only to recall that in the past several decades man has succeeded in unleashing and controlling the incredible power locked with the atom. An even greater achievement has been his ability to voyage to the moon and walk upon its surface. On the basis of these astonishing scientific and technical triumphs alone, it would seem within the realm of possibility that the unpredictable, complex forces of the weather may one day be harnessed. Efforts to accomplish that objective are already being vigorously pressed both in the United States and countries abroad.

There is another aspect to the above question, equally difficult to answer and perhaps more vitally important. This relates to the matter of whether man ought to tinker with such unknown, complicated elements as those involving weather and storms in particular. We will have more to say on this point later on.

Contrary to what many of us might think, the idea of controlling weather is not by any means a modern one. It has been prevalent down through the ages in both primitive and advanced societies. It was common among numerous ancient tribes to have certain individuals who were believed to have special powers for communicating with the gods to bring rain or to stop it, as the case might be.

Some primitive tribes also had special group rites to implore their gods for rain. The performing of rain dances by the American

Indians—especially those inhabiting the semi-arid regions of the country—is a well-documented example.

In ancient pre-Christian times it was the practice of many peoples to shoot arrows at oncoming thunderstorms in the hope of chasing away the dark, ominous clouds. Later, when gunpowder came into wide use, the same practice was continued with rifles, cannon, and even rockets. Historians tell us that explosives were rather widely used in sixteenth-century Europe for the purpose of reducing the damage caused by hailstorms. Guns and rockets were shot into the storm clouds in the belief that the noise from these weapons could fend off the worst effects of a storm. This idea was carried still further by the ringing of church bells whenever thunderstorms approached.

Cannons, guns, rockets, and church bells were all popular as storm-control tools in Europe right up through the eighteenth century. In time, problems arose from their use when people complained that the results—it was never known whether these were real or fanciful—were doing more harm than good. Protests be-

A weather research plane used in Project Stormfury.

came so strong in some countries that guns and rockets for reducing storm damage were forbidden. The ringing of church bells for that purpose was also banned. However, that prohibition was primarily for the safety of the bell ringers, since many were electrocuted by lightning during thunderstorms.

One of the more successful applications of the early use of cannon fire to minimize the destructive work of hailstones took place in Austria late in the nineteenth century. The burgomaster of a district in that country, an enthusiastic amateur weather expert, had a number of cannons placed in the region under his control. When thunderstorms made their appearance, with the threat of hail, he had the cannons aimed at the clouds and fired in salvos.

After one year, farmers of the district reported no damage to crops and all were convinced that the cannon-firing method of modifying a storm, crude and simple though it was, had worked. Since no scientific explanation could be given at the time for the apparent success of this storm-control technique, and the noise and danger of the cannonading were clearly objectionable, the use of these exploding devices was frowned upon by the Austrian government and eventually the firing of cannons for weather-changing purposes was prohibited.

After many years of disuse the idea of employing explosives for altering the destructive effects of hailstorms was revived in our own times. Instead of cannons, however, rockets shot to appropriate altitudes and then exploded among the storm clouds are being used in a number of countries throughout the world. The Po Valley of Italy, where there are extensive vineyards, is one place where the technique is employed on a large scale. Here grape growers shoot thousands of rockets skyward over the course of a year to protect their grapevines from barrages of hail. Rockets are employed by farmers in Russia and Argentina for similar purposes.

A different approach to weather modification is employed by citrus growers in Florida and California when cold or freezing temperatures threaten their delicate crops. Hundreds of heat genera-

155

Hail usually falls from huge cumulonimbus clouds such as this one photographed near Boulder, Colorado. Such clouds, commonly called thunderheads, can tower as high as fifty or sixty thousand feet above the earth's surface.

tors positioned throughout an orchard are used to ward off the cold air.

Motor-driven fans on tall poles are also placed among orange and grapefruit trees and spun whenever a cold snap threatens. The theory behind this is that the spinning fans circulate or mix the cold, heavier air near the ground with the warmer, lighter air above it.

During World War II fog was a serious handicap at military airfields in England. In an effort to combat the problem steel containers of oil and gasoline were placed along the edge of runways and then set afire. The heat tended to evaporate the water droplets in the fog, causing the blinding shroud to disappear.

Most of the methods described so far would have to be classed as non-scientific attempts to change or modify certain aspects of weather. The scientific approach for achieving the same ends began in November of 1946. At that time two American scientists, Dr. Irving Langmuir and Vincent J. Schaefer of the General Electric Research Laboratory, produced a man-made snowfall over the Berkshire Mountains in western Massachusetts. The scientists performed their seeming magic by scattering tiny pellets of dry ice (solid carbon dioxide) onto a super-cooled layer of cirrus clouds. The snowfall was surpisingly vigorous and took place over a wide area.

Dozens of oil-fired heating units like this are used to protect Florida citrus orchards during cold waves.

The large-scale outdoor experiment was a follow-up to laboratory work in the course of which Schaefer first discovered the technique for making artificial precipitation. Working with a deep-freeze chamber, he found that ice crystals could be produced in the cold air of the chamber by introducing a needle-like instrument whose point had been super-cooled. Experimenting further, Schaefer learned that he could obtained the same results by sprinkling the interior of the chamber with a small quantity of dry ice.

About a year later Bernard Vonnegut, a fellow scientist working in the same area of research, discovered that he could produce man-made snow by seeding super-cooled air with silver iodide smoke particles.

When news of these experiments spread, weather experts around the world became greatly excited. They considered them an enormous achievement and a giant stride toward the day when man at last could "do" something about the weather.

Cloud-seeding experiments followed in rapid succession both in the United States and countries abroad. Much of the activity eventually centered on methods for the artificial production of rain. The chief purpose of this work was to bring needed rainfall to parched farm areas. New precipitation elements were tried and techniques for seeding were improved, with such encouraging results that now, in a number of countries, there are private and government agencies that perform rain-making services.

Despite many efforts to make the technique of cloud seeding a practical tool for producing rain, scientists never lost sight of the real worth of that method for research purposes. Throughout the 1950's they employed cloud seeding for a variety of experiments. Thunderstorms were among the earliest and more popular test subjects. The tests did not produce any results of importance except to show the scientists how little they really know about cloud structure and dynamics. They further realized that if they were ever to

Dr. Vincent J. Schaefer (left) and Dr. Irving Langmuir, who pioneered the cloud-seeding technique for weather modification.

be successful in altering weather, especially storms, a good deal more had to be learned about the basic nature and activity of weather.

After a long period of study aimed at acquiring more fundamental knowledge about the elements and behavior of weather, using such modern technological aids as radar, the computer, and satellites, scientists are once again pursuing efforts to modify the weather. Cloud seeding is still the principal method for test purposes in these research programs. Some of the major scientific attempts at modifying weather and storms in particular are being conducted in the United States. One of the more interesting projects, having to do with storm modification, is called Project Stormfury.

Project Stormfury is a scientific program that seeks to blunt the destructive power of hurricanes. Formally organized in 1962, it is a cooperative effort enlisting weather experts, technologists, and flying personnel from the National Weather Service and the United

Hurricane Debbie blew out of the Caribbean Sea area in August of 1969. It served as an experimental subject for Project Stormfury, a scientific attempt to modify or control tropical cyclones. The weather satellite ESSA 9 took a picture of the storm on August 18, several hours after it was seeded. The next day another photo of the hurricane showed it somewhat shrunken in size.

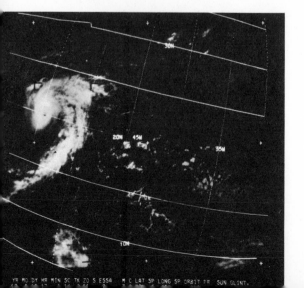
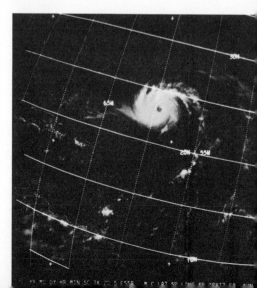

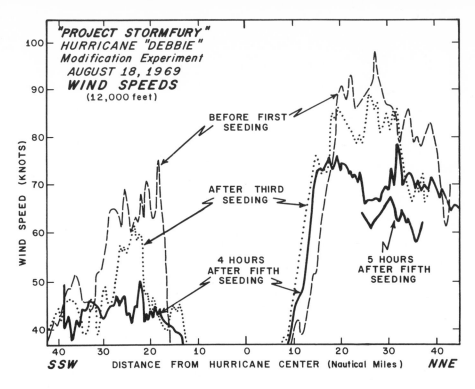

This diagram illustrates the effects of seeding on Hurricane Debbie in the modification experiment, Project Stormfury. Scientists were mildly encouraged by the results.

States Navy. Scientists from a number of universities are also participating. A major portion of the research work is centered at the National Hurricane Research Laboratory, Miami, Florida.

As we know, the hurricane is an enormous powerhouse of energy. It is far more powerful than any force, including the atom bomb, that man has available to counter it. Understanding this, scientists are seeking a weak spot to exploit, an Achilles heel, in the hurricane's structure that might be made use of to reduce the fury of these storms. If any such weaknesses can be utilized even on a small scale initially, extensive changes might be made in the tropical disturbance.

To implement this effort, scientists are carrying out a four-pronged attack. One is aimed at changing the cloud structure swirling around the eye of a hurricane. The object is to cause the incoming warm air to rise higher and faster and farther out from the center of the storm before it can form into a fierce central vortex.

161

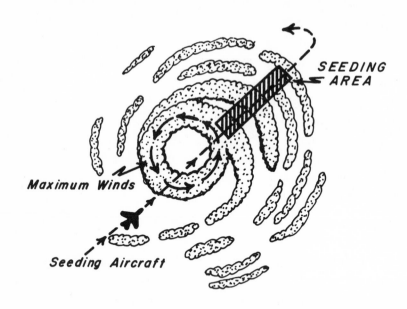

SEEDING AREA

Maximum Winds

Seeding Aircraft

208 SILVER IODIDE GENERATORS DROPPED IN AREA ON EACH SEEDING. (FIVE SEEDINGS ACCOMPLISHED AT 2 HOUR INTERVALS)

The flight path taken by the weather research planes that seeded Hurricane Debbie with silver iodide particles.

If the radius of the spinning wall cloud can be increased, then it is believed the intensity of the whirling winds will be reduced.

Another approach being considered would divert the air flowing into the outer fringes of the hurricane. Still a third idea would seal off the storm's critical energy source, evaporation of sea water within the environs of the storm. This might be accomplished either by coating the ocean surface in the area with chemicals or cooling the surface of the sea, again by using chemicals, or by deep stirring up of the cool lower region.

Still in the realm of conjecture is a final possibility of attacking the power of the hurricane by preventing elements of a disturbed weather condition from forming into a storm. One approach considered would be to create other centers where convective weather forces could be stimulated. Just how these man-made convective centers with rising warm, moist air would be created has not yet been fully worked out. It is hoped that several points of competition for warm air would divert the elements of the original storm enough to prevent it from maturing.

Up to this moment weather scientists in the United States have been concentrating part of their weather-modification research work on hurricanes. They are seeking success mostly by utilizing the first of the attacks mentioned above, involving the cloud-seeding technique. Personnel aboard United States Department of Commerce and Navy weather planes employed for the tests have sown silver iodide particles into the swift-moving clouds of hurricanes and measured the results. The chemical weapon was aimed at the areas just outside of the eyewall, in the hope that the particles would increase the growth of the clouds at the larger radii

The crowded interior of a weather research plane used in Project Stormfury.

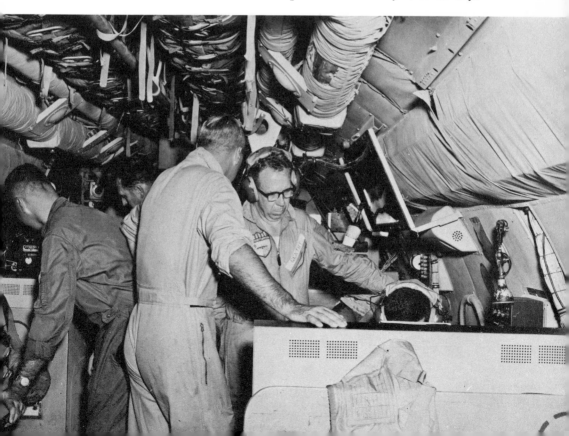

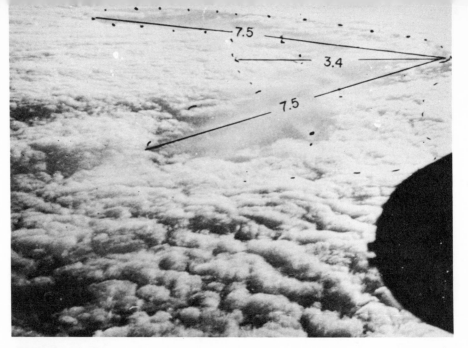

Following laboratory experiments, Dr. Schaefer took his cloud-seeding techniques outdoors. He seeded a cloud layer over the Berkshire Mountains with silver iodide particles from an airplane and made snow fall. The area seeded is shown by the V-shaped marking.

from the center. If the scientific theory was correct, the expansion of the cloud ring would cause some of the low-level inspiraling winds to be diverted from the smaller radius of the wall cloud, thereby reducing their intensity. In effect, they are trying to get the eyewall to expand and to slow down just as a spinning skater slows his spinning by extending his arms.

The silver iodide particles were dropped by means of specially designed flares. As the particles scattered through the cloud layers, the super-cooled cloud droplets were changed into ice crystals. This action caused heat to be released, which in turn made the cloud air warmer and more buoyant. The air's greater buoyancy caused it to rise faster, stimulating cloud growth. If conditions are right, more air enters at cloud bottom, water vapor condenses, more heat is released, and the cloud grows higher until the top reaches up into the outflow layer. Any air entrained in this process never penetrates into the old eyewall, but cycles out of the storm at a larger radius.

164

Early experiments to modify hurricanes by seeding took place in September 1961 with Hurricane Esther and August 1963 with that year's Hurricane Beulah. Both produced little effect on the storms. However, weather scientists had seen enough to warrant continuing their research.

It was not until Hurricane Debbie roared up from the tropics in August of 1969 that scientists of Project Stormfury made a major attempt to modify a hurricane by seeding its clouds with silver iodide. The tropical storm was seeded five times in a period of eight hours on August 18 and again on August 20. At the end of the experiment a definite decrease in the speed of the storm's winds was noted.

Those involved with the work of modifying Hurricane Debbie believed that seeding had diminished the fury of the storm. Only by continued research on other hurricanes, however, will Project

Photo shows two breaks in the cloud layer over the Berkshire Mountains resulting from Dr. Schaefer's outdoor seeding experiment.

Stormfury experts know definitely whether seeding hurricanes actually can reduce their destructive power.

In follow-up efforts to modify hurricanes, weather scientists have been hampered by the fact that these tropical storms have not always come into existence in a good location for test purposes. The utmost caution is taken in the seeding of hurricanes so that one of the storm's more destructive characteristics will not be accidentally intensified. While their knowledge of hurricanes is considerable, the scientists know full well that it is far from complete, and any tinkering with this tropical disturbance must be done with the greatest care.

Largely because of the unknowns, a technical wonder of our time, the computer, is proving a valuable aid. Scientists are using the electronic brain to construct mathematical models of hurricanes. These simulated tropical storms cover the complete range of their existence, from birth to the time of their death. With these models weather experts are able to work out experiments they would like to perform with real storms and so determine beforehand any effects the experiments might produce. Thus, weather experimenters are now able to obtain at least some measure of warning of what the consequences of their actual test efforts would be.

Scientists in the United States are engaged in another area of weather research concerning lightning. They are pursuing this work almost with the same degree of interest as their studies dealing with the modification of hurricanes. As mentioned earlier, lightning kills more people in the United States over the course of a year than hurricanes do. It also starts forest fires, especially in the western part of the United States, that destroy thousands of acres of valuable timberland and vitally needed watersheds. Lightning-caused forest fires in this country average 10,000 annually.

In the face of these somber facts it is no wonder that weather scientists are giving this spectacular destroyer so much research attention. A good part of their efforts are centered in Project

Skyfire, under the guidance of the United States Forest Service.

The basic goal of the studies being conducted by these weather specialists is not only to find out more about the phenomenon of lightning but also to discover ways to suppress it. So far their efforts are being carried out along two avenues of research. The first makes use of seeding the super-cooled parts of thunderstorm clouds with silver iodide particles. Most of the lightning discharges are born in these boiling cauldrons of energy. Earlier tests indicated to scientists that seeding produced myriads of ice crystals within clouds and that these had a tendency to reduce the number of lightning flashes. Just why the crystals should have this effect on lightning is not yet clear. The apparent influence of the crystals was determined from tests extending over a period of five years and by comparison of thunderstorms whose clouds were seeded with those storms whose clouds were left untouched.

Scientists at the New Mexico Institute of Technology are among a number of groups carrying out research relating to the nature of lightning. This radar unit on a mountaintop is an important tool in that work.

A man-made lightning stroke used to study its effects on power transformers.

In an effort to find an explanation that all could agree on, scientists continued their studies in laboratories. They now believe that the incidence of lightning is reduced by the ice crystals because the latter have many sharp points in their structure near which a corona discharge, a glowing effect, takes place. Production of the corona surrounding each individual crystal drains off electrical charges existing within the thunderheads. Deprived of sufficient electrical charge, many lightning strokes therefore fail to materialize.

The second lightning-suppression avenue of research is also based on the corona discharge phenomenon. With this, the corona effect is produced by dropping "chaff"—metallized nylon needles—into the clouds of a thunderstorm. The effect is similar to that produced by ice crystals—short-circuiting the electrical charges within the clouds before they become lightning strokes. The technique of using metallized chaff was originated by weather scientists working for the United States Army.

The chaff approach for reducing the incidence of lightning strokes has not produced any substantial results so far, although the metallized needles have shown that they can create corona discharges. Much more study is needed.

Weather scientists are also exploring ways of toning down the vicious power of that demon storm, the tornado. Because of its nature, odd shape, erratic movements, and destructive intensity, it is not an easy subject for experimental work. Further complicating research on this storm is the fact that weather scientists know so little about it. Despite these handicaps and because tornadoes are so frightfully dangerous, scientists are actively searching for ways to alter these storms.

Several ideas have been suggested for interfering with the formation and development of tornadoes. It must be emphasized that these are strictly ideas, with little or no actual experimental work having been conducted to test them.

One idea or theory would make use of cloud seeding. An over-all storm cloud formation from which tornadoes could spawn would be seeded in various areas with silver iodide. This would freeze water droplets in the clouds, in the process releasing heat. The resulting slight increase in air temperature, it is thought, would interfere with the motion of the storm and prevent the formation of tornado vortices. In other words, if seeding could produce thermal areas or bubbles at strategic points within a storm system, then the storm's energy might be scattered. The theory is that a number of weak rotational elements would be created within the storm, preventing the forming of a single strong vortex which otherwise would have become a tornado.

What they are in need of is some method, seeding or other, for producing buoyant, warm air within a tornado at the proper time. This leads to the problem of finding a convenient tornado to experiment upon.

Another theory for modifying tornadoes would make use of some kind of solar radiation shield to be spread over those areas in which tornadoes have been predicted. The shield would reduce heating of the earth's surface by the sun. Reflected heat from the ground is one of the chief sources of energy for the creation of thunderstorms from which tornadoes are born.

These and other tornado-modifying theories are being investigated by the National Severe Storm Laboratory at Norman, Oklahoma, and other research centers. The weather specialists at these research headquarters have no illusions about the magnitude of the job they have undertaken. Tornadoes are difficult subjects to study. In addition to being extremely destructive, they are of short duration and small size. Also, it is never known for certain where or when they will take place. An enormous amount of time and effort will be needed before anything approaching success can be reported.

In our discussion of storms, we have not considered fogs, as they do not exactly fall into this category of weather disturbances. Nevertheless, they can cause great inconvenience, even

This is a mobile fog-dispersal unit. It is being used jointly by NASA and the Cornell Aeronautical Laboratory in their efforts to find an effective method for dispersing fog at airports.

danger, to ground, air, and sea transportation and other fields of man's activities.

Weather scientists have found that fogs and clouds are alike in their physical structure. Like many of their high-flying cousins, fogs as a rule do not produce rain or other precipitation. There are two main types of fog—warm and cold. Warm fog contains suspended water droplets that are warmer than 32 degrees F. It is this fog that we who live in the temperate regions on earth are most familiar with. As scientists have discovered, this is a most difficult fog to disperse.

Cold fog is classed as a special kind of fog in which the minute water droplets may be colder than 23 degrees F. In contrast to the warm variety, cold fog can be made to disappear rather easily. As a matter of fact, meteorologists have been so successful in finding ways to dissipate this fog that the achievement represents one of their biggest triumphs at weather modification.

The practice of dispersing fog is most commonly employed at commercial airports. Approach lanes and runways that are hidden from the eyes of pilots guiding giant passenger airliners to earth by fog are brought into view by seeding the specific areas with dry ice. The dry ice particles scattered through the fog layer change most of the water droplets into ice crystals which fall to the ground as snow. The fog in the immediate area of the seeding operation either disappears entirely or is thinned out to such a degree that an airline pilot has no difficulty seeing the runway.

In the United States the use of dry ice was first investigated by weather specialists of the United States Air Force and the Army, together with meteorological experts of the United Air Lines. The technique is now used in this country during the winter months when cold fogs are frequent. The method is also used at some European airports.

Scientists have not had similar success with attempts to make warm fog disappear. Seeding was tried but found to have very little effect. Other techniques that have been investigated include the use of devices that discharge heat. This has worked to some degree. The big difficulty with this technique, however, is the need to find a practical way for employing it on a large scale.

One of the most successful methods found for dispersing warm fog has been the use of the downwash from the rotor blades of a helicopter. The strong, earth-directed air currents from the whirling rotors can tear huge holes in the gossamer-like vapors of the fog. The technique has been frequently used in the war in South Vietnam for rescuing United States military flyers whose planes have been shot down.

Reducing the intensity of hailstorms has long been one of man's major weather modification efforts. As we have seen, many of these attempts such as the ringing of church bells and the shooting of cannons have pre-dated the scientific era of meteorology. Today the very latest scientific tools are used to lessen the damaging onslaughts of the frozen pellets of ice. In the United States alone hailstones cause damage to farm crops and property estimated at more than 200 million dollars.

172

Cloud seeding, as we have seen, is one of the modern methods for combating hailstorms. Both in the United States and in countries abroad, particularly Russia, scientists have been quite successful in reducing the formation and fallout of hail by seeding potentially hail-forming clouds with silver iodide particles. These are introduced into storm clouds either with ground-based equipment or from aircraft. Russian scientists prefer shooting artillery shells filled with silver iodide into storm clouds previously studied and believed to contain the characteristics for forming hail. The shells explode at the appropriate altitudes, showering the silver iodide "seeds" through the clouds.

It is believed that the silver iodide particles perform their effective work by serving as nuclei for the formation of countless new hailstones. The hailstones become so numerous that they place an extra demand on the water supply within the clouds. Since this is not sufficient to supply all the forming hailstones, the ice pellets cannot grow to a size or weight that will permit them to fall out of the clouds to earth. The few small hailstones that manage to escape the strong upward-flowing air currents of the storm clouds melt on the way down and end up on earth as rain.

In the United States a vigorous research effort was launched in the summer of 1971 for the purpose of finding an effective way to suppress hailstorms. Called the National Hail Research Experiment, the program will extend over a five-year period. Under the direction of scientists from the National Center for Atmospheric Research at Boulder, Colorado, the project also includes weather experts from several universities, government agencies, and the United States Army. The latter provides personnel skilled in the launching of weather balloons.

Scientists engaged in the weather-modification attempts discussed so far are firmly convinced that only good can come from their researches. They feel that man's existence on earth will be benefited if death-dealing, destructive storms can be diverted or reduced in intensity, or if those areas on earth that are non-

This photograph reveals what can happen when man and hailstorm meet. The plane is an American Airlines DC-6 which encountered severe hail aloft near Guadalupe Pass, Texas.

productive, parched wastelands can be made to bloom by artificial rain-making techniques. In short, these scientists believe that socially and economically the earth can be made a better place for mankind if the weather can be controlled and its disturbances put to work constructively.

Their optimism is not shared by a good many others, both scientists and non-scientists. These doubting Thomases have an equally strong conviction that only harm can come from weather modification. In their view man ought not to be tampering with such enormous and complicated forces of nature. How can weather experts be certain, they ask, that their control techniques with a hurricane, for example, will not backfire and cause the winds of this tropical tempest to blow with greater force or its rain to fall in more torrential quantities?

Their pessimistic attitude toward weather modification is not un-

This cross section of a hailstone, photographed with polarized light, reveals the growth patterns of the ice crystals within the stone.

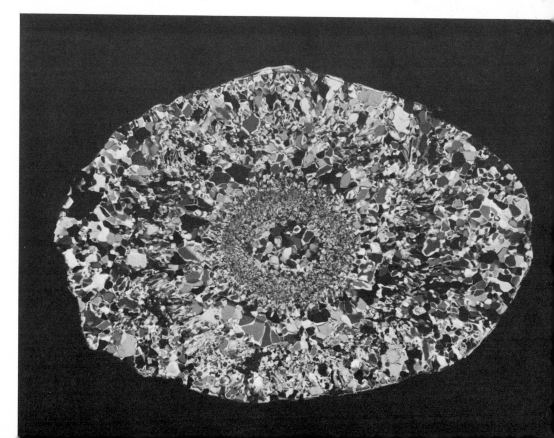

One of the balloons used for taking vertical atmospheric measurements in the lower atmosphere. NCAR scientists use this system in the National Hail Research Experiment (NHRE) started during the summer of 1971.

reasonable in the light of our growing awareness of what man has done and is doing to his earthly environment. In the last decade or so the realization has been brought home with stunning impact that not everything man has achieved in science or technology has been of benefit to his surroundings. In a number of instances, what were at first hailed as triumphs over nature—uncorking the secrets of the atom, for example, or the development of potent chemicals for combating agricultural insect pests—are now being re-evaluated. Indeed, some insecticides have been found so destructive of the environment that their use is banned.

The cumulative effect of the by-products of modern technology has been to poison the air, the land, and the sea to such a degree that man must stop the pollution or else, in the not too distant future, face the fact that life on this planet may well be in its final stages.

And so it is with the whole matter of weather modification. Where only good is sought, unforeseen harm could be the consequence. It is reassuring, therefore, that with all their optimism and confidence of eventually succeeding in their endeavors, weather-modification scientists are fully aware that their researches are tinged with peril. They realize that what they could do accidentally, like unleashing some undesirable long-term weather effect, could be catastrophic to man's sources of food, his health, and even his general environment. Because of the hidden and exposed pitfalls that exist along the various paths of weather-modification research, scientists are treading their way very slowly and with the utmost caution.

Hurricane Names

This is a semipermanent list of girls' names used to identify hurricanes originating in the Atlantic Ocean, Caribbean Sea, and the Gulf of Mexico. The list was prepared in 1960 by the Weather Bureau, now the National Weather Service. A separate set of names is used each year, beginning with the first name in each set and continuing alphabetically. After four years, when the four sets have been used, the sets are used over again in the same manner.

Names of major hurricanes—like Betsy in 1965, Beulah in 1967, and Camille in 1969—are retired for at least ten years and others substituted. Since names beginning with Q, U, X, Y, and Z are so few, they are omitted from the list. Girls' names are also used to identify typhoons and hurricanes in the Pacific.

1970   Alma, Becky, Celia, Dorothy, Ella, Felice, Greta, Hallie, Isabel, Judith, Kendra, Lois, Marsha, Noreen, Orpha, Patty, Rena, Sherry, Thora, Vicky, Wilna.

1971   Arlene, Beth, Chloe, Doria, Edith, Fern, Ginger, Heidi, Irene, Janice, Kristy, Laura, Margo, Nona, Orchid, Portia, Rachel, Sandra, Terese, Verna, Wallis.

1972   Abby, Brenda, Candy, Dolly, Evelyn, Frances, Gladys, Hannah, Ingrid, Janet, Katy, Lila, Molly, Nita, Odette, Paula, Roxie, Stella, Trudy, Vesta, Wesley.

1973   Anna, Blanche, Cindy, Debbie, Eve, Francelia, Gerda, Holly, Inga, Jenny, Kara, Laurie, Martha, Netty, Orva, Peggy, Rhoda, Sadie, Tanya, Virgy, Wenda.

Beaufort Scale

BEAUFORT SCALE OF WIND FORCE
WIND EFFECTS AT SEA *

Wind Force Beau. No.	Knots (Nautical Miles Per Hour)	Wind Description	Probable Wave Height (in feet)	Effects at Sea
0	0–1 (Less than 1)	Calm	——	Sea smooth and mirror-like.
1	1–3 (1–3)	Light air	¼	Scale-like ripples without foam crests.
2	4–6 (4–7)	Light breeze	½	Small, short wavelets; crests have a glassy appearance and do not break.
3	7–10 (8–12)	Gentle breeze	2	Large wavelets; some crests begin to break; foam of glassy appearance. Occasional white foam crests.
4	11–16 (13–18)	Moderate breeze	4	Small waves, becoming longer; fairly frequent white foam crests.
5	17–21 (19–24)	Fresh breeze	6	Moderate waves, taking a more pronounced long form; many white foam crests; may be some spray.
6	22–27 (25–31)	Strong breeze	10	Large waves begin to form; white foam crests are more extensive everywhere; may be some spray.
7	28–33 (32–38)	Near gale	14	Sea heaps up; white foam from breaking waves begins to be blown in streaks along the direction of wind; spindrift begins.

BEAUFORT SCALE OF WIND FORCE
WIND EFFECTS AT SEA *

Wind Force Beau. No.	Knots (Nautical Miles Per Hour)	Wind Description	Probable Wave Height (in feet)	Effects at Sea
8	34–40 (39–46)	Gale	18	Moderately high waves of greater length; edges of crests break into spindrift; foam is blown in well-marked streaks along the direction of the wind.
9	41–47 (47–54)	Strong gale	23	High waves; dense streaks of foam along the direction of the wind; crests of waves begin to topple, tumble, and roll over; spray may reduce visibility.
10	48–55 (55–63)	Storm	29	Very high waves with long, overhanging crests. The resulting foam in great patches is blown in dense white streaks along the direction of the wind. Over-all appearance of the sea is white. The tumbling of the sea becomes heavy and shocklike. Visibility is reduced.
11	56–63 (64–73)	Violent storm	37	Exceptionally high waves that may obscure small and medium-size ships. The sea is completely covered with long white patches of foam lying along the direction of the wind. Everywhere the edges of the wave crests are blown into froth. Visibility reduced.
12	64–71 (74 and over)	Hurricane	45	The air is filled with foam and spray. Sea completely white with driving spray; visibility very much reduced.

* Adapted from National Weather Service Chart.

BEAUFORT SCALE OF WIND FORCE
WIND EFFECTS ON LAND *

Wind Force Beau. No.	Miles Per Hour	Knots	Wind Description	Effects on Land
0	Less than 1	Less than 1	Calm	Smoke rises straight up.
1	1–3	1–3	Light air	Smoke drifts gently, shows direction of wind; wind too weak to move wind vanes.
2	4–7	4–6	Light breeze	Wind felt on face; leaves rustle; directional wind vane is moved.
3	8–12	7–10	Gentle breeze	Leaves constantly moving; small flag extended by breeze.
4	13–18	11–16	Moderate breeze	Dust raised; loose paper blown about; small tree branches moved.
5	19–24	17–21	Fresh breeze	Small trees in leaf sway; small crested waves form on inland waters.
6	25–31	22–27	Strong breeze	Heavy tree branches in motion; wind whistles through electric power and telephone lines; almost impossible to use umbrellas.
7	32–38	28–33	Near gale	Large trees in motion; difficult to walk against wind.
8	39–46	34–40	Gale	Breaks off small branches of trees; difficult to carry on outdoor activities.
9	47–54	41–47	Strong gale	Slight structural damage begins; roof shingles blown off.
10	55–63	48–55	Storm	Trees uprooted; considerable damage to homes and other structures.
11	64–73	56–63	Violent storm	Widespread damage to trees, utility poles, and structures.
12	74 and over	64–71	Hurricane	Extensive damage to trees, power and communication lines, homes and other structures; lives endangered.

* Adapted from National Weather Service Chart.

Glossary

Air Mass   A large body of air, the greater portion of which has a unified horizontal structure.

Anticyclone   An atmospheric system from the center of which winds spiral out in a clockwise direction in the Northern Hemisphere and counterclockwise in the Southern Hemisphere. More popularly called a high, it generally brings good weather.

Circulation   The large, basic wind-flow patterns of the atmosphere, like the westerlies of the middle latitudes.

Convection   The action of upward-rising warm air brought about by an atmospheric disturbance, such as from the meeting of cold and warm fronts.

Coriolis Force   The apparent force created by the earth's rotation. It deflects wind flow to the right in the Northern Hemisphere; to the left in the Southern Hemisphere.

Cyclone   Any atmospheric system in which atmospheric pressure decreases progressively to a minimum value at the center. Winds blow in toward the center, counterclockwise in the Northern Hemisphere; clockwise in the Southern Hemisphere. The system is frequently referred to as a low.

Doldrums   A region of calm or very light variable winds in the equatorial zone.

Gale   A wind force blowing 39 miles per hour or more.

Hurricane   A tropical cyclonic storm with winds blowing at least 74 miles per hour. It has distinctive spiraling rain clouds swirling around a comparatively calm eye.

Hurricane Eye   The center of a tropical cyclone with near calm wind conditions, few or no clouds, and no precipitation.

Isobar   On the weather map this represents a line that connects points of equal atmospheric pressure.

Lightning   The visible display of a flow of current that is a secondary effect of the electrification that occurs within a thunderstorm cloud system.

Spiral Band   Long, narrow cloud bands spiraling within the wind system of a hurricane.

Squall Line   An advancing horizontal line of clouds producing thunderstorms or rain squalls along its extent.

Surge   A sudden, fast rise in the water level along a seacoast. It comes almost simultaneously with the approach of an offshore storm.

Thunder   The sound produced by explosive expansion of air heated by the rapid passage of a lightning stroke.

Tornado   A violently rotating funnel-shaped column of air that descends to earth from thunderstorm cloud systems.

Vortex   A spinning wind system, especially its center.

Waterspout   A swirling, rotating tornado that occurs over oceans and inland waters.

Suggestions
for Further
Reading

Atkinson, Bruce W. *The Weather Business*. Garden City: Double-
day & Company, Inc., 1969. (Paperback)

Dobson, G. M. B. *Exploring the Atmosphere*. Oxford: The Claren-
don Press, 1968. (Advanced, but selected chapters are good.)

Dunn, Gordon E., and Miller, Banner I. *Atlantic Hurricanes*.
Baton Rouge: Louisiana State University Press, 1964. (Rev.
ed.)

Flora, Snowden D. *Tornadoes of the United States*. Norman: University of Oklahoma Press, 1954. (Rev. ed.)

Tannehill, Ivan Ray. *Hurricanes*. Princeton: Princeton University
Press, 1944. (Old but still excellent.)

————. *Hurricane Hunters*. New York: Dodd, Mead & Co., 1954.

National Science Foundation. *Weather Modification,* Tenth An-
nual Report, 1968. Superintendent of Documents, U. S. Government Printing Office, Washington, D.C. 20402. (65 cents)

Index